BRENDA COURT~~~~~ ~~~~~ ~~~~~
up on Merseyside. She is married to a Church
of England clergyman and has two sons, but
stresses that the church of St Cuthbert and
its parishioners described in this book,
though true-to-life, are entirely fictional. Her
own story was told in her previous book, *Not
Quite Heaven*. She and her family now live in
Northamptonshire, where her husband
teaches in a public school and is licensed to a
village church, while Brenda is a tutor in
creative writing and runs a writers'
workshop.

Brenda Courtie

❋ JENNY'S YEAR
The calendar of a vicar's wife

TRI∧NGLE

First published 1986
Triangle
SPCK
Holy Trinity Church
Marylebone Road
London NW1 4DU

ACKNOWLEDGEMENTS

Bible quotations are from the Revised Standard Version of the
Bible, copyrighted 1946, 1952 © 1971, 1973 by the Division
of Christian Education of the National Council of the
Churches of Christ in the USA, and are used by permission.

All places and characters in this book are imaginary and
do not portray any real location or actual living persons.

British Library Cataloguing in Publication Data

Courtie, Brenda
    Jenny's year: the calendar of a vicar's wife
    1. Church of England—Clergy   2. Clergymen's
    wives—England—Religious life
    I. Title
    248.4'830435   BV4395

    ISBN 0-281-04215-2

Typeset by Pioneer, Perthshire
Printed and bound in Great Britain by
Hazell Watson & Viney Limited
Members of the BPCC Group, Aylesbury, Bucks.

Contents

❖ Introduction

To look at our house, you'd think it was a haven of peace. Big, old Victorian vicarage, it is, with far too much garden. But the lawns and the tall trees do remind you of gentler days gone by.

To look at my husband, you'd think he was quite unflappable. Well, he's tall and dark and sort of reassuring looking. And then, of course, there's the dog-collar.

To look at our two sons, you'd think they were normal growing lads. A bit boisterous, perhaps, but nothing malicious.

And there's me. Your average unexceptional not-so-young mum.

Picture us, if you like, on our front steps. You might think, 'What a fortunate family, living in such an idyllic situation, cut off from all the frantic hassle of the world outside.' Actually, it's not quite like that . . .

1 September

✤ Ashes to Ashes

On the last day of the school summer holidays, I had some mending to do. I'd just got the sewing machine out on the kitchen table and was threading it up when I heard Charles looking for me.

'Jenny?'

'Kitchen!'

Soon his head appeared round the swing door that separates my department from the hall.

'Sewing?'

'Joshua's school trousers,' I said. 'The ones that used to be Drew's. They're four years out of date and the boys go back to school tomorrow.'

'Thank goodness.' Charles feigned relief, letting the door swing behind him as he crossed the kitchen to look out at our old garden where croquet and afternoon teas have long since given way to cricket and barbecues. 'I suppose they're out there now, making the most of what's left?'

I had to answer through a mouthful of pins: 'Drew's out there burning rubbish somewhere, but Josh is in his bedroom making an invention.'

'Don't tell me — another cardboard slot-machine for conning pennies out of indulgent aunties!'

I removed the pins. 'Something like that,' I nodded. 'Only this one's meant to dispense sweets, I think. Are you going out?'

'Yes. I've just popped in to tell you. I'm calling to see the Bensons' new baby, and then if I've time I'll go on to Bishop's Court.'

He noticed my frown. 'Didn't I mention it? The bishop thinks he's found me a curate.'

'No,' I said slowly, as I carefully machined along the pinned seam. 'I'll believe it when I see it.'

He came and kissed the top of my head. 'Cynic! Anyway, I'll try to be back for a cup of tea before Mrs Nelson comes to lay old Albert's remains to rest.'

I'd almost forgotten that.

'Oh yes,' I said quickly. 'The undertaker brought the ashes this morning. They're in the hall.' We've learned to be business-like about these things.

'Fine,' he said. 'I'll pick them up later.' Then he remembered something else. 'Jenny, I've sorted through all that jumble out there, and I've managed to get it into two cartons instead of four. You can tell Josh he can have the empty boxes if they're any use to him. 'Bye for now.'

The door was still swinging when Joshua, our ten-year-old, thundered down the stairs and crashed into the kitchen.

'Hi Mum! Where's everybody?'

I glanced up from my sewing. 'Josh, must you come down stairs like a wild elephant? I'm here, Drew's having a bonfire, and Dad's out doing his visits.'

He jumped his bottom on to the table and swung his legs. 'Rats! I was looking for someone to help me with my invention.'

I knew what was coming.

'Mum, I don't suppose you've got a minute?'

'Right in one,' I said to him. 'If I don't get this sewing finished, you'll be going to school in your pyjamas. How *is* the sweet machine, anyway?'

He pulled a face. 'Bit of a flop. Well, a lot of a flop really. Keeps flopping all over the place. First of all Mark One collapsed. Lack of staples. We've run out.'

'I'm not surprised, the rate you get through them. Was there a Mark Two?'

'Yes. I remodelled the old Mark One with some insulating tape Dad found in those boxes of jumble. But now the cardboard's so bent about it won't stay rigid, and the sweets keep dropping out before you can get your money in.'

Light dawned. 'Ah, I see! Free sweets!'

'Yes,' he grunted, 'and that wasn't the intention.'

'Never mind, Josh,' I encouraged. 'Dad says you can have those empty cartons in the hall if you like.'

He catapulted off the table shouting, 'Great!' and rocketed through the swing door. Mark Three was about to go into production.

The next hour was pretty quiet, I admit. Sort of calm before the storm. Just three phone calls. A wedding enquiry, then Canon Fletcher wondering where the monthly chapter meeting was going to be, then the local paper wanting to know if we were doing anything newsworthy. With an efficiency born of experience, I took the bride-to-be's number and said Charles would call back; I checked the desk diary and found the canon's meeting at St Philip's; and I tried to make the new playgroup sound like the scoop of the year.

After that, I got the first pair of trousers finished.

It was as I was starting the second pair that the front doorbell rang. Before I could push my chair back to answer it, Drew came in from the garden. 'OK Mum. I'll get that.'

I wrinkled my nose at the smoky aroma that floated through the kitchen after our fourteen-year-old. Mercifully, he was wearing his oldest jeans and jumper. Drew once tended a bonfire for the whole of a Sunday afternoon, still in his best Sunday morning clothes. It got him out of going to Evensong and Joshua reckoned he'd done it on purpose.

In time with the swing of the door, Drew came back into the kitchen. 'Mum, it's old Pongo, your tramp. He wants a cup of tea. Where's Josh?'

'Upstairs reconstructing his sweet dispenser,' I said, as I got up from the sewing machine for the fourth time. 'And Pongo Rafferty's not *my* tramp, especially. He's common property. And if you're staying indoors, Drew, for goodness' sake get changed. You smell like a used firework.'

Drew nodded cheekily towards the swing door and retorted with a grin, 'You ain't smelled nothin' yet! Go and get a sniff of old Pongo!'

'Drew!' I growled at him, and I pushed through into the hall. When I opened the front door, though, I had to concede that the smell in the porch would obliterate Drew's current odour entirely. I was forced to take a step back to keep my nose in touch with a more breathable atmosphere. Pongo Rafferty is a harmless old man of the road. He calls fairly regularly at our house, never in exactly the same set of clothes, but always looking as if the whole outfit is welded to him with several years' dirt. He gave a toothless grin from behind his lavatory brush beard.

'Afternoon, ma'am. I was just thinkin', with it bein' so warm, yer might be havin' a cup o' tea about now?'

'Of course,' I said brightly. Well, as brightly as I could without breathing. 'I'll just put the kettle on.'

I retreated into the hall, and noticed a pair of gents' shoes at the top of one of the boxes of jumble clothes. So I opened the door again and held them at arm's length.

6

'Someone's given us these for the jumble sale, Mr Rafferty. Would you like to try them on while you're waiting?'

Our vicarage tea-for-tramps system is to serve the caller, then ask him just to leave the mug in the porch when he's finished. So once I'd taken Pongo his tea, I got back to my sewing.

Soon I was joined by a sweeter-smelling Drew. I fancied I recognised my talc, but thought it prudent not to mention it. He had collected Pongo's mug, and as he rinsed it under the tap he said, 'Mum, there's a pair of smelly old boots by the front door.'

'Oh heavens, they'll be Pongo's old ones. I gave some shoes from the jumble. Drew, go and put them on your bonfire, would you?'

'But Mum!' he objected, 'I've just changed into clean things.'

'Well, they'll have to be burned, Drew. They're a health hazard.'

'I think parents are a health hazard. They drive you potty!'

Still, he grudgingly went off to collect the boots. 'Roll on school. No tramps. No mothers . . .'

At last I finished the second pair of trousers.

I'd put the machine away and refilled the kettle, and was just getting the milk from the fridge when Charles called 'Hello' from the hall, and almost immediately appeared in the kitchen.

'Hi there! Had a quiet afternoon?'

I laughed. 'You've got to be joking! In this house?'

'Well, did you get your sewing finished?'

'As a matter of fact I did, in the gaps. What about you? Any sign of a curate?'

He came and sat at the table with a bit of a grimace.

'Oh, I don't think so. This chap the bishop's trying to place only wants a part-time appointment while he's writing a PH D about early liturgies or something. Any calls?'

I recounted the phone calls and Pongo's visit.

'I gave him some shoes from the jumble. Drew burned the smelly boots on the bonfire.'

Charles put down his cup with a start. 'Which reminds me. Where did you say you'd put Mr Nelson's ashes?'

'In the hall. On the chair by the coat cupboard.'

'No. They're not there. I looked on my way in.'

I got up. Mother to the rescue as usual. We went into the hall together. The two boxes of jumble were alongside the front door. The chair by the hall wardrobe was empty. I must say, that threw me.

'I was absolutely sure I put the box on this chair,' I said, not altogether helpfully.

Charles was tapping his fingertips together, a sure sign of his patience thinning. 'Come on, Jen. Mrs Nelson will be here any minute now.'

I frantically tried to summon a mental recap of the day's events, but was interrupted by Joshua thudding downstairs.

'Hi Dad! Thanks for the boxes!'

Boxes? Oh no!

'Josh!' I shot at him, 'did you see those ashes the undertaker brought this morning? They were in a little cardboard box on this chair.'

Josh looked very guilty. He took a step backwards up the stairs again. 'Oh. Oh gosh. I'm sorry, Dad.'

Charles was desperate.

'Merciful heaven, Josh, *where are they?*'

Josh took a deep breath, and with the protection of the banister rail between him and us he confessed.

'You see, Mum said I could have the empty jumble boxes, and they were great. Only I needed a smaller one to hold the sweets in my machine, and . . . '

Charles exploded. '*Heavens, child! What did you do with it?*'

Retreating still further, Josh continued in the even tones of one facing certain death.

'I thought it was rubbish. I asked Drew to tip the ash stuff on his bonfire with Pongo's boots, when he came up for his old clothes. He brought me the box back just now when he came up to get changed again. Sorry, Dad.'

There was a brief silence while the full horror penetrated his father's consciousness.

Then Charles panicked. He turned to me, waving his arms like a stricken windmill. 'Sorry! The boy's sorry! Mr Nelson's remains on a bonfire, the box in a slot-machine, and he's *sorry*!'

Josh tried a tiny repair job. 'Er . . . Mr Nelson won't exactly know, will he?'

Charles spun round to him. 'It's not *Mr* Nelson I'm worried about, you clown. *Mrs* Nelson's due here right now to watch me bury Albert's ashes in the Garden of Rest!'

Throughout this exchange I'd been biting on my thumb knuckle, trying to come up with some solution. I reckoned there was an outside chance of a reprieve.

'Josh, is the box still OK?'

'Yes. It's only got sweets in. It's sort of suspended inside the machine.'

'Then fetch it. Quick!'

He raced on his errand, glad to be out of the dock.

Charles turned on me with a quiet disbelief bordering on derangement. 'Jenny,' he whispered, 'I don't bury empty boxes. I bury *ashes*.'

I tried to pacify him. 'Yes, darling, I know. Now don't you worry.'

I ignored his bulging eyes and shouted up the stairs for Drew. The boys appeared on the landing together.

'What's up, Mum?' Drew asked. 'Why's Dad banging his head on the wall like that?'

Poor Charles. I had to leave him to manage his own breakdown while I instructed the boys.

'Drew, I want you to go down to your bonfire again.'

Now it was my son's turn to question my sanity. '*What?*' he bellowed. 'Aw Mum! I've only just finished getting changed again! Every rotten time I get into clean clothes, I have to rotten get back into rotten smoky ones.'

He ran down the stairs and leapt into a dramatic pose at the bottom. 'Presenting Andrew 'Smoky' Belvidere, Quick Change Artist! Da- daa!'

Charles, forehead pressed hard to the wall, muttered 'Heaven preserve us.'

I hustled the boys into the kitchen and thrust a large sieve at them. 'No time to change. Got the box? Rake up some cool ashes and sieve them into it. And be quick!'

Drew blinked. 'What for?'

'Drew. *Do it!*'

I pushed them into the garden just as Charles staggered into the kitchen. He dropped heavily into a chair.

'Jen, I can't do it. I'll be burying the wrong ashes. Year after year dear Mrs Nelson will come here to weep over the remains of . . . well, of some old garden rubbish!'

'What do you suggest, then?' I snapped. The tension was telling. 'You can hardly tell her the truth. That Albert's remains finished up on the bonfire with Pongo's old boots. Besides, *some* of the ashes will be his.'

I shouldn't have said that.

Charles shouted back at me, 'Oh fine, just fine!' Then in a fluty parsonic voice I've *never* heard him use in practice he intoned, 'We have entrusted our brother Albert Nelson to God's merciful keeping, and we now commit *some* of his ashes to the ground. Along with an assortment of charred grass cuttings, singed eggboxes and Pongo Rafferty's old boots!'

The boys burst in, and Drew put the box on the table in front of Charles.

'There! Josh told me all about it. I reckon Mrs Nelson won't know the difference, Dad. Only don't let her hold the box. It's still warm. She'll think old Albert's just arrived hot from the crematorium!'

'*Drew*!' I screamed, and the doorbell rang.

'Mrs Nelson!'

Charles grabbed the box and glared at the boys. 'Listen, you two. Not a word of this to anyone, do you hear? If the parish knew I was burying Pongo's boots in consecrated ground . . . if the bishop knew I was praying over them . . . Merciful Heaven!' he wailed, and pushed through into the hall.

Twenty minutes later I was washing a salad at the sink when he returned.

'How was it?' I asked. I turned to examine his face and he grinned his lovely, normal boyish grin, just like Drew, and sat himself on the table, just like Joshua.

'Jen, it was incredible. Before I could get properly started, Mrs Nelson said she wanted a word with me. I thought for a minute she'd found out, but of course she hadn't .'

'What then?'

'She said she couldn't bear to think of her husband's ashes shut away under the ground, and would I mind if we just scattered them over the vicarage garden.'

I couldn't believe it. The *vicarage* garden?

'Why?' I demanded. 'Why not the Garden of Rest?'

'Well, apparently her Albert was very fond of this old place. Used to help the gardener here when he was a lad. When vicarages had gardeners.

'And croquet lawns and orchards,' I nodded, looking beyond the window to our well-worn playground.

'So she thought he'd like to be back here, where he was happy, in the vicarage garden. With the trees, and the flowers . . .'

'. . . and the bonfire!' I finished for him.

The doorbell rang, and Drew called, 'OK — I'll get it.'

I dried my hands on the teatowel. Who on earth would be calling at teatime?

Drew came into the kitchen, biting on a laugh. 'You'll never guess,' he said. 'It's old Pongo back again. He says the shoes pinch and please could he have his boots back!'

We all roared, and Charles sprang from his perch on the table. 'Poor old Pongo! I'll have to go and tell him they've been burned.'

Then he reflected for a moment. 'No I won't,' he said. 'I'll tell him they've been reverently dispatched to that Happy Tramping Ground in the Sky. With all the benefits of full church rites!'

As he pushed through the swing door, Drew shouted after him, 'You could tell him you saved their soles.'

So there we are. All's well that ends well. Charles was going to put the boys' pocket money into the missionary box as a punishment, but I pointed out that they had saved the day in the end. So he relented.

Mind you, he was pretty shaken by it all. So much so that when the bishop phoned later for a definite 'yes' or 'no' about the egghead curate, Charles said 'yes'. And immediately wished he hadn't.

12

2 October

✦ All Good Gifts

From our kitchen window you can just see the back of the church over to the far right of the garden.

I was watching when Charles came out of the vestry after the early Communion. He locked the door behind him, then stood and smiled up appreciatively at the warm October sky. 'Yes,' I thought to myself, 'it *is* a nice day for Harvest Festival.'

He thrust his hands deep into his cassock pocket-slits and strolled along the gravel path towards the vicarage.

Suddenly he stopped.

'Now what?' I wondered.

Charles was looking across the grass to the ancient apple trees in what remained of the old orchard. He seemed undecided about something. I saw him take a quick look at his watch, then he strode briskly across the lawn and bent to pick up an apple from beneath one of the trees.

Poor Charles. This year's apples were a washout, and he usually takes basketfuls into church for Harvest. But after a quick inspection he dropped his apple. Others were similarly examined and thrown down to remain where they lay, surrounded by the confetti — white, pink and brown — of small pieces of fruit in varying stages of decay. He kicked aimlessly at this litter, then walked slowly to the kitchen door with despondent shoulders.

As he came in, I pushed the swing door into the hall and called, 'Dad's back! Breakfast!'

I went across and threaded my arms round his waist while he washed his hands at the sink. 'You're looking glum,' I said. 'Anything in particular?'

Charles pulled a towel from its perch above the boiler.

'Been looking at the apples. Do you know, there's not a one fit to go into church? And when you think how the vicarage apples usually fill all the gaps. I just wish I knew what's been at them.' But I knew it wasn't just the apples.

He sat down at the table and nodded at the extra chair. 'And it's young Timothy Ball's first Sunday. You know, Jenny, I'm not sure I should have asked him to preach at the main service. In fact, I'm not sure I should have let the bishop talk me into having him at all. What good is a part-time academic in a city parish like this?' He waved a spoon in a gesture of appeal at the kitchen walls.

'Sh-sh! He'll hear you!' I scolded him, as I slipped the cosy on to the teapot. 'And anyway, remember what the bishop said. Half a loaf is better than none.'

Charles pushed two slices of bread into the toaster.

'Yes. But what if the half-a-loaf turns out to be half-baked?'

'Charles!'

My reprimand was drowned by the entrance of Drew and Josh, tumbling through the swing door.

'Hi Mum! Hi Dad!'

'Sorry we're late. We weren't sure your yell would reach the flat so we went up the top stairs and banged on the door.'

As they settled at the table and stretched for the cereals, Charles lectured them, waving his spoon again.

'Now, you two. I've told you. You're not to pester Timothy. Just remember, he's got a PH D to finish and leave him alone.'

The swing door pushed open again and the Reverend

Timothy Ball came into the kitchen, looking about as comfortable as an apprentice in brand new overalls. He'd been with us a week, but this was the first time I'd seen him in his working clothes. A slim young man with gold-rimmed spectacles, the pallor of his fair hair and colouring was severely emphasised by the black of his new cassock. He swallowed nervously, and his Adam's apple gave a resentful push against the unfamiliar dog-collar.

My maternal instinct gave an inner lurch. 'God help him, he's so young.' I began to understand Charles's misgivings.

'Good morning everyone. Am I late?'

Charles remembered to smile as he said, 'No, no, Timothy. We haven't started. Come and sit down and I'll say grace.'

But he declaimed the familiar words with a new earnestness. 'For what we are about to receive, may the Lord make us truly thankful.' He caught my glare of reproof when he opened his eyes after the 'Amen'.

We launched into cereal, and Josh announced through a mouthful of crispies, 'Don't call hum Tumothy, Dad. He doesn't like it.'

Charles's eyebrows high-jumped.

'Oh? I'm sorry. Do you prefer Tim?'

The curate hesitated, mouth open, spoon in mid-flight. Drew spoke for him. 'No, Dad. It's Moth.'

While Charles frowned his incomprehension, Drew grinned and continued, 'Moth. Moth Ball. They found some in his Moses-basket when he was a baby and it stuck. Good, isn't it?'

I smiled, but Charles choked. 'Sorry,' he coughed. 'Cornflake! Gone the wrong way!' He grabbed at his tea and looked at me to bail him out.

'You mustn't let the boys tease you, Tim,' I said as

kindly as I could. 'Charles has already warned them.'

The curate smiled. 'No, really!' he said. 'Everyone calls me Moth. I told them about it yesterday.' He turned to Charles and asked, 'I hope you don't mind?'

Charles, now recovered, shook his head in good-natured disbelief.

'Of course I don't mind. If that's your usual handle, we'll all use it. Moth it is!'

And I relaxed as breakfast proceeded with a little more ease.

When all was cleared away, Charles took his new colleague into the garden for his opinion on the devastation of the fruit.

I arranged the pans of vegetables on the cooker, ready to switch on after church, and when I'd put the meat in the oven and set the timer I wandered into the garden too. The autumn sun was warm on my face as I crossed the grass, and the quiet tranquillity of the city Sunday was not at all threatened by the men's low voices.

'They're all like that,' Charles was saying. 'Great chunks hacked out and abandoned, not even eaten. What d'you think?'

Moth examined the apple he was holding before speaking. Then he said, 'It's got to be a bird. A big bird, hasn't it?'

'Mmm,' Charles agreed. 'Perhaps a magpie. Or even a wood-pigeon from the park?'

'Bigger than that, I'd say. Look at the size of the bits. Whatever it is has got a pretty big beak.'

It was sounding very sinister!

'Something out of Alfred Hitchcock, Moth?' I asked.

He turned and smiled shyly, and Charles went on, 'Why isn't it eating the fruit, d'you think?'

Moth examined another apple and said, 'I expect it is

16

eating some of it. But it seems to be after the seeds, really.'

'Mmm. A large-beaked, seed-eating bird.' Charles rubbed his chin thoughtfully.

Suddenly there was a rustling sound in the leaves above my head.

'Keep still,' Moth hissed. 'It's in the tree!'

I froze, fully expecting to be lifted Sinbad-style by the claws of some gigantic feathered monster.

Charles's eyes narrowed as he searched the leaves. 'What on earth is it? Can you see it, Moth?'

'No. *Yes*! It's green. Look, just there.'

He pointed and I lifted my gaze to the branches above my head. As a beady eye met mine, a voice snapped, 'Do it again! Do it again!'

Charles jumped. 'What the . . . ?'

But I'd seen it. 'Look, Charles! It's a parrot! An apple green parrot!'

We all laughed with relief, then as the bird flapped madly to a higher branch, Charles said, 'Keep an eye on it, Moth. I'll call the police and see who's lost it.'

I walked back to the house with him. That bird must have been in our apple trees for two or three weeks! It was still screeching at Moth, 'Do it again! Do it again!'

'A parrot?' yelled Josh when we told the boys. 'Wow!' And the two of them lunged through the kitchen to see for themselves.

I followed Charles into the study where he picked up the telephone and dialled the local police station. After a pause, he said, 'Hello? Charles Belvidere here. Vicar, St Cuthbert's. No, no trouble. Just a lost and found enquiry. Has anyone reported a missing parrot?'

He turned to me and rolled his eyes.

'*Parrot*!' he repeated. 'Yes, I know it's Harvest Festival and yes the church *is* full of unclaimed vegetables, as you so aptly describe them. But I said *parrot*!' A pause, then, 'Yes, that's right. In our apple trees.' Another pause, then, 'I'll tell you what it's doing there. It's pecking the living daylights out of every blessed apple!'

I risked a gentle touch on his arm. It worked.

'Sorry, officer. It's just that this stupid bird's sabotaging my Harvest.'

The word prompted him to glance at his watch. 'Look. If you'd be so kind as to check your book . . . Thank you.' He drummed his fingers on the desk. 'Mrs. Burrows. Windermere Street. Six, three, five, nine. Thanks very much. Goodbye.' He pressed the cradle and dialled again, muttering, 'Let's hope they're at home.'

Charles went back to Moth and feathered friend, and less than ten minutes later I opened the front door to a very small girl embracing a very large bird cage.

'Me gran's sent me for Percy,' she announced.

I took her through to the back garden, where she repeated for Charles's benefit, 'Me gran's sent me for Percy.' She crashed the cage down alongside the bird-watchers.

'She's awful sorry 'e's been such a nuisance. 'E's been missin' for weeks. She told me ter give yer this.' She pulled a note from her anorak pocket, but Charles protested.

'No, honest, Vicar,' the child insisted, 'put it in yer collection. She's that relieved . . .' And the little girl turned her attention to the parrot. 'Get down 'ere this minute, yer daft thing, or I'll come up there an' pluck yer!'

We smothered a few smiles between us and Josh nudged Drew appreciatively.

'Do it again! Do it again!' yelled Percy.

'Which being interpreted,' ventured Moth, 'means "go

and boil your head"! Look at him. He's no intention of coming down.'

'We'll see about that' said the girl, and she bent over the cage to lift out a battered, tin tea-caddy. 'Pin yer ears back, Perce!' she called, and she shook the tin.

It rattled.

'It's 'is seed,' she told us smugly.

'Do it again! Do it again!' demanded the bird. So she rattled the tin once more, then opened it and placed it in the cage.

With an aristocratic disregard for his plebeian spectators, Percy parrot strutted along first one branch, then another, until he was just above his cage. He hopped on to it and, using his beak as a pivot, swung himself through the doorway with the grace and skill of a Russian gymnast.

We cheered. 'Home at last!'

'Do it again!' yelled the bird from his swinging perch. Then he hopped off to attack the tin of seed.

We watched him for a while, admiring his lovely plumage, the green becoming blue as he turned this way and that.

Finally Charles said to Moth, 'Come on. We ought to be over in church.' They walked across to the vestry, and I was left to thank Percy's rescuer.

'I hope he's none the worse for his stay here. Perhaps you'd better take him home now.' And I waved her through the front door again, bird cage in arms.

I quickly forgot all about parrots as I grabbed my handbag and hymn book and eventually dashed across the grass for the Harvest Festival service.

'Praise him for the harvest store, he has filled the garner floor,' sang the packed church. I found a seat at the end of a pew and glanced up at Charles. He looked fairly cynical, and I could guess what he was thinking. 'No he hasn't. A darned parrot got there first!'

Our new curate picked his way through the carrots and onions to the pulpit. He seemed paler than ever. He cleared his throat and began.

'Hello. Doesn't the church look lovely today?' He waited. 'Well, doesn't it?'

A few children shouted, 'Yes!' Moth relaxed visibly and continued.

'And why does it look so lovely? What special day is it?'

His young audience obliged with, 'Harvest Festival!'

'Of course! Tell me, who brought all these splendid things to make our church so lovely?' A forest of hands waved in response. 'Thank you, all of you. And where did you get all these super things?' The word 'shops' broke in a wave across the pews. 'The shops? What? Did nobody grow anything?'

There was a crop of nervous giggles. Few of our parish's terraced houses have gardens. I saw Charles wince slightly. 'Oh dear,' I thought. 'Our first *faux pas*.'

Then an elderly gentleman near the front called out, 'I grew that marrer,' and he pointed to a prize specimen on the floor beside Charles's stall. Charles was obviously relieved. He leaned over and picked the thing up, and held it triumphantly over his head.

As he bent to put it down again, a familiar voice seared through the laughter. 'Do it again! Do it again!'

Percy! Charles sat up with a start, and glared at the front pew. I craned my neck to see what he'd seen. The little bird-catcher, and alongside her, Percy in his cage. Charles's face was thinly-disguised rage.

'Oh heavens!' I moaned inwardly. 'That feathered pest is determined to spoil Charles's Harvest.'

But Moth seemed almost to welcome the interruption.

When the laughter had subsided, he leaned over the front of the pulpit and said matily, 'Hiya Percy! Fancy an apple?' This time Charles laughed, too, with a sigh I knew said, 'If you can't beat them . . .'

Moth carried on.

'You know, I've only been here a week, but I did want to grow something for today. I found a packet of seeds that said "very fast growing" and I planted a few in this big pot.' He turned to look at the chancel steps, and there, right on cue, were Josh and Drew, positioning a large lidless plastic dustbin.

I'd been vaguely disquieted at not seeing them in their usual place in the choir, but I'd supposed they'd been too late to robe and were sitting somewhere in the congregation. Now I realized that they and Moth had been cooking something up. It was obvious that Charles knew nothing of it. He leaned forward in his seat to see what was going on. Somehow, I wasn't at all nervous for Moth now. He was completely in control. I had the feeling he would soon surprise both his congregation and his vicar. I sat back in my pew to watch.

'Nothing's happened yet,' Moth continued, 'so I think we'll play a little game while we wait.'

And the curate began 'I—spy', handing out large cards to children who spotted harvest produce beginning with the specified letter.

'Grapes!'

'Oranges!'

'Dates!'

A row of children was collecting in front of the pulpit, each holding up a large card with a letter on it. Obviously there was going to be some text or message spelt out. Charles folded his arms and smiled his approval.

Suddenly there was a rustling from the dustbin, and we

21

all ooed and aahed as the most enormous yellow flower burst out above the rim.

'Do it again! Do it again!' Good old Percy.

From my pew quite near the front, I could see that the flower was actually several twelve-inch petals cut from yellow plastic foam, all stuck to a black and white football. Joshua's, I guessed. The flower nodded gently, and I watched Charles bend his head to peer under the great bloom, to see how the thing was supported, and by what device it had been made to spring up. It appeared to have a stem made from green rope. But I couldn't see anything else. I was pretty sure Charles couldn't either.

When the hubbub died down, Moth grinned at the congregation.

'There!' he said, 'it's started to grow. Let's get back to our game.'

'Marrow!'

'Apples!'

'Daisies!'

'Eggs!'

There were a few comprehending nods as people worked out the words on the cards. 'GOD MADE . . .'

Then a child's voice pierced the mutters: 'Quick! Look be'ind yer!'

Moth obediently turned to look at his plant. The giant flower was actually growing taller. Charles was shaking slightly as he chuckled in his stall. The football rose slowly, petals gracefully flapping as the green rope stem lengthened beneath it. Unfurling from the swaying stalk were several crumpled tissue paper leaves.

The children and Percy were wild with excitement.

'Do it again! Do it again!'

'It's magic!'

'No. There's a kid in the bin!'

'It's the Indian rope trick!'

'Grandad! Grandad! How does he do it?'

I now knew the answer to that one. Only eyes accustomed to the gloom of the Victorian sanctuary and chancel would be able to spot it. A fine nylon thread, Drew's fishing line I guessed, was attached to the top of the football, and was itself suspended from a point lost in darkness in the roof.

Charles looked my way and winked at me. So he'd spotted it, too. His eyes led mine to the tracery round the organ. There the thread came in from the roof somewhere and disappeared through the stonework. 'So that's it' I thought with a smile. 'A pulley in the roof, and an accomplice, or two, in the organ loft.'

'We really must finish our game!' said the curate with mock severity, and I half wondered whether we might charge an admittance fee for Moth's next appearance.

'Icing sugar!' Icing sugar? At Harvest? Something else planted by the curate, no doubt.

'Tomatoes!'

'Grapefruit!'

'Radishes!'

'Onions!'

'Water!'

'And what have we got on the cards?' Moth leaned over the pulpit to look at his little assistants.

With one voice the congregation read, 'GOD MADE IT GROW!'

Then, as if to order, Moth's flower produced a tremendous spurt that took it, waving delicately, to a height of twenty feet, amid loud cheers.

'*Do it again! Do it again!*' By this time, Percy had picked up some followers.

Finally Moth called for quiet.

'I hope this will help you to remember', he said, 'that no matter where our food comes from, the shops or the garden,' and he paused to glower at Percy, 'we should have no food at all if it weren't for the power of our loving Heavenly Father. Your mum bought the cabbage. Our friend here planted his marrow and cared for it. But remember, God made it grow.'

The new curate dismissed his helpers and announced the next hymn.

As the timbers of our old church roof now rattled to the mighty strains of 'All good gifts around us are sent from heav'n above,' I glanced at Charles. He was looking across at his half-a-loaf and smiling in total agreement.

3 November

❈ Gunpowder, Soup and Potatoes

November the fifth dawned damp and overcast. Rain before nightfall was an absolute certainty.

Charles dolloped marmalade on to his toast. 'Just as well we decided against a parish bonfire,' he said.

'But Charles,' I reminded him from the littered notice board, where I was frantically hunting for a sponsor form Josh should have returned to school at the end of October, 'you can't set off *fireworks* in the rain either. And you can hardly take a parish fireworks party into the church hall.'

'*If* it rains,' he countered with commendable optimism, 'we'll serve the soup and baked potatoes in the hall, and dash in and out between showers for the fireworks.'

'Well, *I'm* not washing the church hall floor tomorrow, mate,' I warned him, and I charged through the swing door with Josh's form in my hand.

The boys were almost ready to leave for school. Josh was fastening his duffel coat.

'It would be easier with your gloves off.'

And Drew was stuffing heaven knows what into his bag.

'You're going to school, Drew, not on a round-the-world hike!'

I shoved the form into Josh's pocket and he clattered down the front steps.

From the drive Drew called, 'Hey! Look at this.' 'This' was a complete but ancient car wheel with a very flat tyre.

The vicarage garden is a convenient rubbish dump for some of our locals.

'Put it over by the garage', I yelled. 'And I'll ask the dustmen to take it. Then run, for pity's sake, or you'll be late!'

''Bye Mum.' Josh waved from the gate. 'Keep your eye on Flossie, won't you?'

We could have done without Flossie, today of all days. But I'd promised old Mr Garnett months ago we'd have his dog while he went to have his cataract op. It was just unfortunate that the eye hospital should have sent for him this week.

Flossie was an aged, smooth-haired terrier, well trained and harmless. Normally she was no trouble at all; we'd had her before. But her hearing was as yet unimpaired, and each November the fifth the bangs and swishes of the fireworks terrified her to the point where she forgot her arthritis and just dashed around in panic, crashing heedlessly into tables, plants, bookshelves, you name it. Doggie tranquillisers were ineffective, Mr Garnett had ruefully assured us. Someone would have to sit with poor Flossie during the fireworks party and just hang on tight. I hadn't said anything to Mr Garnett, but I'd secretly decided to try a pair of Boots' earplugs. For Flossie, I mean. Nothing ventured, etcetera.

As I went back into the kitchen to clear up, our faithful friend lifted her head and gave me a toothy grin. I stooped to her basket by the boiler and tickled her tummy. 'Don't worry, old girl. We'll get you through today one way or another.'

The heavens opened at coffee time and the rain continued relentlessly into the afternoon. At about three o'clock Flossie and I took a cup of tea along to Charles in his study.

'Darling,' I said tentatively as I passed him the chocolate digestives, 'do you think we ought to put the word around, fireworks party cancelled? There's still the municipal one in the park if people are really keen.'

'Rubbish!' he said. And he meant it.

In fact, Charles was looking quite smug by half-past five, when I was gathering up my contributions towards the planned soup and potato supper.

'See?' he grinned at me. 'Rain's stopped. I reckon we're in for a really splendid evening.' And he went off to the sitting room to watch the TV news.

He closed the door behind him, but it slowly swung open again, as was its wont. He'd been promising to fix the catch for weeks. Anyway, I clearly heard him singing, 'Oh what a beautiful evening!'

Flossie didn't like the earplugs. Not even when I'd warmed them on the boiler. She rolled around, pitifully rubbing her ears on the floor, so of course I took them out.

'Well, you'll just have to grin and bear it then,' I warned her. 'But the boys are taking turns to doggysit so you'll be all right.'

For all that, I still had my fingers mentally crossed as I threw on my mac, grabbed my carrier bag and went off across the garden to the church hall.

Now, try as I may, there's one group of ladies in our parish I just can't persuade to call me Jenny. They're the Ladies' Guild committee. Somehow, being their chair-person has invested me with a reverence I should prefer to be without. The Playgroup Mums call me Jenny. The Senior Citizens call me Jenny dear. But to the Ladies' Guild committee I'm always Mrs Belvidere.

'Oh good, here's Mrs Belvidere now.'

It was Edna Jones doing the soup.

'You're the chicken, aren't you?'

27

I thought, 'There's no answer to that,' but I said, 'Yes Edna. There's a catering pack in this carrier. Is the oven on for the potatoes?' And with the other ladies I set to, preparing a warm supper for the hardy few who might brave the weather in the hope of parish fireworks.

As it happened, even before the first 'golden rain' had been lit, we were besieged at the hatch by some wet and bedraggled parishioners wanting to know was the soup ready yet.

'Oh dear,' Edna muttered. 'Looks like the rain's back. They'll all be in now, Mrs Belvidere, just you see.'

She was right. Soon, the church hall was full of folk in steaming anoraks and messy wellies, cheering their dampened spirits with plastic cups of soup and tinfoil-wrapped baked potatoes. We were kept very busy in the kitchen serving all-comers at the hatch, and still they were pouring in at the hall's main door.

'I didn't expect our parish do to be so popular, did you, Edna?'

'Must say I didn't,' Edna answered from behind a tray of cups. 'Specially considering the weather. I hope it goes off soon so's they can have their display.'

I was hoping it would go off soon before we ran out of soup. We'd already started serving the potatoes in halves. I poured some boiling water on the chicken noodle, and threw in a couple of stock cubes I'd pressed Drew to fetch from the vicarage. 'Lord,' I prayed beneath my breath, 'I'm not sure the hall can hold five thousand, but if it does we'll need a bit of a miracle. I've only got two cubes left and the shops are shut!'

The miracle was that the rain stopped again almost immediately, and the happily warmed-up crowds made their way out into the garden for the main event.

'You coming, Mrs Belvidere?' Edna tied a headscarf round her ears as she spoke.

'I don't think so, Edna, thank you. I'll have five minutes' peace and then I'll start on the saucepans.'

'Well, leave us the drying up, then.'

And the Ladies' Guild committee went off to see the show.

Left on my own, I pottered about, gathering up the used soup cups. Now and then the hall flooded with extra light, flaming pink or ghostly green. I jumped a couple of times when the bangs were over-loud. The crowd outside roared, laughed, screamed and ooed. One or two little ones were crying.

Then I heard it.

A dog barked. And not just once. Several frantic barks ran into a baskerville howl.

'That's Flossie!' I yelled to no one but myself, and I dashed out of the hall and ran round the side to our garden.

I was immediately taken aback by the size of the crowd. Where on earth had they all come from?

'Excuse me, please. Would you excuse me? Can I come through?'

I picked my way through a wall of total strangers who were standing in the rhubarb quite unmoved by Flossie's wails. She was out. No doubt about that. But she didn't seem to be running about. The howls were all coming from the one place, somewhere over by the garage, if only I could get there.

Totally unaware of Flossie's noise and my dilemma, Charles and Moth carried on with the rockets.

'Swish . . . crack-crack!'

'Oooh!'

'How-owl!'

Where were the boys? What had happened to the doggy-sitting?

At last I emerged from the scrum and ran across to the garage. Framed in the light streaming from the side window of the vicarage kitchen was an amazing tableau. It consisted of Josh, a policeman, two ambulance men and three firemen, all talking at once. Centre stage, howling, was Flossie. She had her tail in the air and her head right down, as if she were sniffing at something at the foot of the garage wall. But in fact I couldn't see her head at all, because she'd pushed it through something. That old car wheel the boys had found on the drive! The heavy steel hub circled her neck like a collar.

Poor Flossie! I knelt down to hold her tight.

'All right, Floss. It's all right.'

I wanted to talk into her ear, but I couldn't find it. It was through the car wheel with the rest of her head. I lifted the wheel, with some effort, away from its angle against the wall and looked round the tyre at her.

When she saw me she grinned. Then another rocket exploded and she set off howling again.

It took twenty minutes for the firemen to cut her free. By that time, the fireworks had finished, the crowds had gone, and so had the police and the ambulance.

While Moth cleared up outside, the family gathered in the vicarage kitchen for an official enquiry. Charles was chairman. His eyes flashed from Josh to Drew and back again.

'Right! What happened?'

'Nothing to do with me,' said Drew. 'It was my turn to be outside.'

Josh nervously fingered the toggles on his coat as all eyes fixed on him, Flossie's included. But when we heard his story, we had to agree it hadn't really been his fault.

Apparently, he'd gone to answer the front door bell, someone asking the way to the fireworks, leaving Flossie in the sitting room. But of course, the door didn't close properly behind him, ('Yes, I *know* I said I'd mend it' Charles said sheepishly), so Flossie followed, and took off into the garden with Josh in hot pursuit.

Somewhere in the front bushes they'd encountered a cat, also in a state of panic. Cat ran for garage, followed by Flossie, followed by Josh. Seeing what looked like a cat-sized refuge, cat jumped through centre of old car wheel. Followed by Flossie's head, which stuck firm. To her great concern. And cat's great delight. Cat ran off, and Josh raced back to the house to phone the fire brigade, giving them some garbled tale about an accident in which a certain Flossie had her head stuck fast to the wheel of a car.

Drew rolled his eyes. 'No wonder they fetched the ambulance; you made it sound really gruesome!'

'Fortunately the firemen saw the funny side,' Charles reassured me. 'But they'd have been cross if it hadn't been such a wet day.'

'Why? What difference would that have made?'

'Well, normally on bonfire night they're chasing about all over the place dealing with dangerous fires. The rain gave them an easy evening.'

That raised another problem that had been bothering me.

'Charles, where did they all come from? All those people? In such bad weather?'

Drew chipped in, 'Oh, that was me.'

'You? How?'

'There were lots of people walking up to the park to the public fireworks, but not many coming to ours. So when it started raining I stuck a notice on the church notice board saying "Parish Fireworks. Free Soup In Hall." And they all decided not to walk any further in the wet. Even if the public show was a washout, it meant the church one was a big success!'

Charles exploded. '*Drew*! We gave up free-soup-evangelism decades ago!'

'I know,' said our cocky teenager. 'Great shame, too, when you see what a good time they all had. Only it's called public relations now, Dad.'

Before Charles could think of a suitable response, Josh piped up again. 'Anything to drink before bed, Mum?'

'Oh yes,' I said. 'There's an awful lot of chicken noodle soup with no noodles.'

'No noodles?'

So I told them. 'Noodles take an extra miracle, and I think we've had our share for one evening.'

They all assumed the excitement had gone to my head. And maybe it had!

4 December

✻ Ding Dong Merrily

It was after Evensong on the first Sunday in December. I'd decided to collect the men's surplices from the clergy vestry to put them in with Monday's wash.

As I knocked and walked in, Moth was hanging his cassock in the robes cupboard.

'Is this the week the organ tuners are coming?' he asked.

Charles reached across for a hanger and answered him. 'Yes. Wednesday. It'll only be a quick blow on the dust, though. The Organ Fund couldn't finance a proper overhaul. And yet, if we don't have it done soon, the wretched thing will rot beyond recall. What we need, Moth, is a thundering big donation.'

I said nothing myself. But as I gathered up the two surplices, I was pretty sure of what would follow. Moth's eyes twinkled as he spoke.

'Er . . . I've been thinking about that.' And he prepared to launch an idea he'd already chewed over with me that afternoon while I was preparing tea in the kitchen.

'You see, my brother Tom is a churchwarden at Little Tuckton. It's very county over there, no money worries at all. I thought I might ask him to invite our choir to sing carols at some of their big houses. You know, in aid of some worthy charity, e.g. Organ Fund in Depressed Downtown Parish. What d'you think?'

I leaned on the old safe, as anxious as Moth to hear just what Charles did think.

'I'll tell you what I think. I think it's moral blackmail, sending our lot over there to help the landed gentry appease their upper class consciences.'

Moth blanched, and I was about to protest on his behalf when Charles laughed and said, 'But it's a jolly good idea for all that! Catch Miss Langford and sort it out with her.'

'Ooh you!' I chided, and I ruffled his hair with the bundle of laundry, while Moth dashed off on his mission.

Miss Langford owns the 'Haberdashery and Drapers' shop opposite St Cuthbert's. She's small and plump with fluffy grey hair tinted blue, and cupid's bow lips painted pink. On Sundays, however, her dextrous fingers turn from ribbons and knitting needles to the weekly battle with our ancient pipe organ. And as carol singing was an obvious way to boost the Organ Fund, she was naturally delighted with Moth's idea.

So it was that the following Thursday evening I found myself rounded up with the specially-formed Christmas choir in Miss Langford's crooked little flat above the shop. Our regular church choir has teetered for years on the borders of extinction, but Moth managed to charm several people into his money-raising project.

There was Beryl — tall, thin, forty and unmarried, who was self-appointed leader of the trebles despite being a martyr to sinusitis. She'd brought along two girls from the office, and the three of them occupied a large chintz sofa, with Josh and Drew stuffed between them in lieu of cushions.

On the upright chairs beside the upright piano sat Mr Greenwood from the corner shop next to our church hall, and Mr O'Brien, our occasional verger, known to all and sundry as 'Irish' O'Brien.

Moth sat with them, prepared to sing either tenor or bass, whichever might need extra volume.

In the armchairs were the altos, that is to say myself, and Rita Macdonald who runs the playgroup.

Moth nodded and blushed as Miss Langford thanked 'young Mr Ball' for his kindness in arranging the proposed tour, then the *ad hoc* ensemble warmed up on 'While Shepherds Watched'. All things considered, it didn't sound too bad. There were enough trebles to drown Beryl's nasal efforts, and Rita and I held a fairly confident alto line. Mr Greenwood's bass seemed loud and sure, so Moth settled on the tenor with Irish O'Brien.

From the piano, Miss Langford called for the next carol on the sheet. "Silent Night', please, everyone. Same as usual. Trebles only in verse two, and everyone else will hum.'

I drew breath, ready to sing, then spent it again as Mr Greenwood spoke out suddenly.

'Speakin' o' hummin',' he said, 'I'm not comin' if them Barlows 'as ter come!'

While Mr Greenwood glared his challenge at Miss Langford, I silenced my sons' giggles with an eloquent stare of my own. The rest of the company studied their carol sheets closely.

For some reason, Mr and Mrs Barlow had missed this rehearsal. Perhaps Miss Langford had conveniently forgotten to tell them about our grand tour? But insofar as we've ever had a regular choir at St Cuthbert's, the Barlows are regular choir members.

They're also something of a parish joke.

Middle-aged, eccentric, untidy and unwashed, they've managed to rear an enormous brood of lookalikes. Those of them who haven't officially left home yet are intermittently 'away' at various reformative institutions. But chasing respectability with the singlemindedness of a lepidopterist, Mrs Barlow drags her husband to church every week to sing with her in the choir. Not that 'Father', as she calls him, can be said to sing as such. Poor man can't even read. He just moos his way through Mattins or Sung Eucharist with his book upside down as often as not.

However, I knew on this occasion that it wasn't the Barlows' singing Mr Greenwood was objecting to. The problem had been highlighted by Mrs Barlow herself one memorable Sunday morning when they'd dashed into church just as the choir and clergy were about to process out of the vestry. 'Mother's' apologies had reverberated off the old stone walls. 'Sorry we're late, Vicar. It's Father's fault. 'E would go back an' wash!'

Mr Greenwood's obvious fear was that on the night of the tour of the very grand houses, Mr and Mrs Barlow might *not* wash.

Moth, bless him, saved the situation before we could fret too much.

'I'm afraid the Barlows couldn't manage the tour,' he announced. 'They tell me they're spending Christmas with a married daughter.'

This wasn't the time to explain to our curate that none of the Barlow girls had actually gone in for marriage as such. But it did mean that on the big night a week before Christmas, Mr Greenwood graced the outing with his presence and his booming bass voice, and so our special Christmas choir climbed into the battered old parish minibus and set out into the frosty darkness, heading for Little Tuckton's affluent acreage.

We came first to Rickleton Farm, the home of Moth's brother Tom. He'd asked us to call fairly early so that his children could join in the carols before going to bed.

The farmhouse was really a tudor manor, and we were ushered into a large oak-panelled entrance hall dominated by an enormous log fire. We were introduced to the toddlers, Justin and Lisa, all rosy and shiny from their bath. They were wrapped up in their dressing gowns, and after Uncle Moth had duly kissed and tickled them, they lolled together on a high-backed wooden settle.

I followed the other visiting minstrels as they arranged themselves around the tall Christmas tree, and we sang, without accompaniment, 'Away in a Manger' and 'Once in Royal David's City'.

Then Tom's wife, Meg, brought in a steaming bowl of hot spiced punch 'to keep out the cold'. As we congregated gratefully around the punch bowl, I noticed old Irish shuffle with his drink across to Tom at the fire.

'I was t'inkin', sir, as 'ow the kiddies would like to hear me bells, like.'

I was not the only surprised onlooker as Irish lifted a suitcase on to the hall table and drew out eight gleaming handbells, all different sizes. Moth rubbed his nose nervously as Irish set them down in order. The old verger took a long drink of punch as a kind of inspiration, then chimed his way through 'The Bells of St Mary's' without a falter. The old boy had obviously invested in a new hobby.

Moth gave me a knowing look which said, 'Trust him to keep this a secret until now!' But the children were ecstatic, and our hosts insisted on an encore in exchange for another glass of punch. So Irish further delighted the assembled company with, of all things, 'Cockles and Mussels'. I felt we were losing hold of the Christmas spirit. To make matters worse, Mr Greenwood started to sing when it came to the chorus.

At the end of the song, I was quietly relieved when Moth smiled brightly and enthused, 'Well done, Irish! Now let me help you to pack them away or we'll be late at Hadley.'

Irish glowed. A combination, I suppose, of pride, punch

and the proximity of the log fire. But as we bundled ourselves back into the minibus I did wonder if we'd solved all our social problems with the disposal of the Barlows.

Moth remained buoyant. 'That was a good start', he shouted, swerving the vehicle along the dark country lane. 'Tom gave me a cheque for a hundred pounds!'

Josh and Drew cheered, and almost immediately the bus swung into the drive up to Hadley Manor.

Here, the welcome was as cold as Rickleton had been warm.

Hadley is a Georgian house. A Palladian portico opens into a long entrance hall broken halfway down by a wide marble staircase. I felt no obvious heating to combat the draughts. The carpet was threadbare and the silk wall covering was faded and torn. Against the long wall facing the stairs was a row of tall chairs, on which were seated the assembled household of Hadley Manor.

Lady Hadley was on the centre chair, a frozen-faced old lady in a long black dress with a high collar. Moth had told me about her. She was the last remaining mistress of all this genteel poverty, with no successors. So either side of her sat her staff, the housekeeper and two domestics to her right, the butler and gardener-handyman on her left.

'Perhaps you would care to use the stairs?' came the arch summons.

We obediently tiered ourselves opposite milady, and shaking with nerves and cold we gave our command performance: 'Angels from the Realms' and 'Ding Dong Merrily on High'. Fortunately the stair-well above our heads gave quite a lift to our strained voices. The free echo made our efforts quite impressive.

Coffee was served. Moth drank his purposefully stationed in front of Irish's suitcase. But old Irish was as cowed as the rest of us, presumably reckoning that our hostess wouldn't be likely to indulge in a rousing chorus of 'Cockles and Mussels'.

Back in the minibus I was overtaken by curiosity and called, 'Did she give us anything, Moth?'

'A tenner!' was his reply.

'Mean old faggot!' came Mr Greenwood's frank comment.

Moth looked round briefly. 'Let's look on it as the widow's mite, shall we?'

Dear Moth.

We drove on in silence.

The ride up to Tollingham House was hysterical, not to say reckless, because Moth had quite forgotten the newly-installed ramps intended to slow approaching vehicles. 'Blast!' he cursed loudly. 'Tom warned me about these sleeping policemen.' I heard Josh shriek with delight and Drew shatter his illusions. But the incident was enough to cheer our spirits again, and there was plenty of laughter as we finally tumbled out on to the brightly-lit forecourt.

Tollingham House is Victorian Gothic, all turrets and church windows. According to Moth, it was built by one Sir Henry Aspull, a wine importer. Now it's the home of his grandson, Sir George, whose astute direction of the family business has netted him a small fortune.

It was Sir George who met us at the porch. 'Come in, come in!' he sang. 'We're all in the dining room. You're just in time for the port!'

I managed to clamp my hand over Josh's 'Yippee!'

Tollingham dining room was large, warm and comfortable. The wide bay window was curtained in appropriately wine-coloured velvet. The long regency table was red mahogany.

Sir George's wife, Lady Margaret, pushed back her chair to greet us.

'Do come in. Yes, and take your coats off. It's quite warm in here. Now, this is our daughter Caroline, and her fiancé Clive Sherrington. I think George is getting you something before you sing.'

We happily joined Sir George in the bay, where he was dispensing drinks from a tray on the grand piano.

'Here we are! Port for the adults, port and lemon for the boys.'

My eyes forestalled any comment from Josh on these arrangements.

After 'Good King Wenceslas' and 'Silent Night' (with hum), another couple crept into the room. Domestic staff, I guessed. The lady wore an apron, at least. Anyway, they were discreetly given drinks and seated at the dining table with the family. It was becoming quite a party.

In the easy atmosphere we happily sang through half a dozen carols before Sir George plied us with further refreshment. 'Who's for another drink? You're certainly singing for your supper tonight. Oh good, Mrs Picket's brought in the mince pies. That's right. Pass them round. Now, let me top up those glasses!'

In the midst of all this jovial bonhomie, I saw Moth grow suddenly pale. I looked around and felt my stomach tighten. Irish had vanished! The old rogue had embellished the last two carols with several ill-disguised hiccups. Surely he hadn't shamed us all by passing out?

There was a commotion under the grand piano. Irish's voice drifted up. 'Sorry, your lordship. Didn't see your foot there.'

I began to panic. What *was* the idiot *doing*?

Irish answered as if in reply to my query. 'I'm just unpackin' me handbells, like. T'ought you an' your missus might fancy a little recital.'

The combined protests of Moth, Miss Langford and

myself were no match for Sir George's enthusiasm. Soon the bells were lined up on top of the piano with Irish standing over them, swaying gently from side to side. I looked down at my port and watched its firelight flickers as I swished it round the glass, waiting for the worst.

This time he started with 'Cockles and Mussels', made only two mistakes, and sang loudly in the choruses to encourage the others.

'Bravo! Bravo!' laughed Sir George, and he refilled Irish's glass. Moth and I stared at each other, wide-eyed and helpless, dumb with apprehension. Or sheer terror.

Meanwhile, at the dining table, the family were all laughing and applauding. The traditional Christmas carols had given way to 'Irish O'Brien in Concert', and the curate resorted to mouthing silent prayers. Or silent oaths.

'An' now,' Irish announced, still swaying, 'before I goes on ter give yerz me *other* number, I'm tellin' yerz. Dis is not for no Organ Fund. Dis is for the poor old retired donkeys!' And while we all reeled under the impact of this sudden revolt, he began jingling the opening phrase of 'The Bells of St Mary's'.

The warm room, the crackling logs, the good port and the sentimental melody had a soporific effect on all except Moth and me. The ladies closed their eyes and half sang the odd word here and there. The men swayed and hummed. I alone, it seemed, noticed that something was awfully wrong. No. Miss Langford had spotted it too, but Moth's glazed expression communicated nothing to indicate whether he had or not.

When Irish reached the next to last line of the song, which is exactly the same as the first line, instead of going into the impressive ending, the beaming Irishman had continued as if the song had only just begun. I thought it wisest not to say anything. Perhaps it was intentional.

Surely Irish would call a halt after two verses? But no! Once again, the maestro of the handbells dodged the ending and found himself back at line two of the song.

This time Sir George noticed. I saw him look across at Moth and wink reassuringly. As the end of the song came up for the third time, like a drowning soul yelling for rescue, our host moved to stand alongside Irish, singing as he manoeuvred. His rich, aristocratic voice grew louder and louder until he lurched into the last line at a bellow.

'*Those wedding bells ring out, ring out, for you—and—me!*'

Of course, Irish followed him on the handbells as if on automatic pilot, and they finished together in harmony, like a couple of old troupers. The Tollingham household cheered with genuine delight. I just clapped with relief. Miss Langford gathered up the song sheets ostentatiously, and Moth brought the suitcase out from under the piano and deftly packed the handbells, muttering under his breath.

Back in the bus, Irish was snoring before we hit the second sleeping policeman.

Moth took Sir George's envelope from his pocket and passed it to Mr Greenwood.

'You open it,' he said. 'I daren't look.'

'Well I'll be . . . !' gasped Mr Greenwood. 'There's two cheques in 'ere. Five hundred pounds for the Organ Fund. And *another* five hundred for the blessed retired donkeys!'

The old bellringer beamed in oblivion.

5 *January*

✲ Saints and Martyrs

'I see it's jungle-training time again?' said Charles.

It was wash day. A grey rain and sleet wash day.

'If you mean the damp stuff steaming on the radiators,' I said, 'yes it is. I'm sorry, darling. But it's the only answer when the weather's like this.'

He filled the kettle while I folded the last of the towels on the kitchen table. 'If I promise to tell you when the bishop's coming,' he went on, 'will you promise not to have your briefs and my pants festooning the hall in greeting?'

I swung round in alarm. 'The *bishop*?'

Then I saw his smile. And caught it with a well-aimed, wet face cloth.

After he'd kissed me, he said, 'I've just had the matron of Brecondale on the phone. Guess who went and helped with the old folks' Christmas dinner?'

I spooned coffee powder into the mugs.

'No idea.'

'Helen and Sophie.'

'Oh?'

A niggle at the back of mind was suddenly eased.

'So that's where she was,' I said. 'You know, Charles, I don't think I believed Helen when she said she'd be busy Christmas Day. I thought she was too proud to accept our invitation. Just goes to show, doesn't it? Wrong again!'

'A godsend, Matron called her. And I gather little Sophie was top-of-the-bill. The residents plied her with chocolates and tickles all day and the good child wasn't even sick!'

Yes, a good child indeed. But I was thinking of Helen.

'Charles, do you think I might ask Helen to help with our church Senior Citizens' party? I mean, if she's got a soft spot for old people . . . well, you know how hard it is to get helpers.'

'You can only ask, sweetheart. Go round and sound her out.'

So I did.

We'd known Helen for almost a year. She'd brought baby Sophie to be baptized, and when Charles tactfully asked about other relatives he found she had no one else. Her parents were dead, and the grandmother who raised her died just after Helen came north to study graphic design. Upset and vulnerable, she'd fallen headlong for an older art student whose pursuits took him to Italy as soon as he learned she was pregnant. She wasn't yet twenty, and was now living on social security in a damp flat above a corner shop in our parish.

Although I called to see her fairly frequently, I never met, or even heard Helen mention, the two students who'd been Sophie's godparents. So I was surprised when our young friend had insisted she couldn't come to us for Christmas. I had to assume that she'd perhaps arranged to visit a friend of her grandmother's.

As she opened the door to me, Helen's smile countered the musty smell of the damp stairway behind her.

'Oh, hi Jenny. Come on up, I'm just about to have a coffee.'

'No, not for me, thanks Helen, I've just had some with Charles,' I said as I followed her up the stairs to her flat. 'I've only come to ask a favour.'

She fastened the safety-gate behind us and took me into her little sitting-room. It was warm and welcoming, despite

44

the January gloom outside. Helen's artistic eye and clever fingers had drawn together the shoestring décor and furnishings into a comforting blend of plum, pink and beige. But my eye went instinctively to the bulbous wallpaper in the far corner.

'I'm trying to keep it up with drawing-pins,' she said with a hopeless shrug. 'Silly to think of it, really. The plaster's so crumbly they keep dropping out.'

'Still no joy from the agent?'

'No. He just sends his man for the rent. And of course, *he's* no idea who the owner is. Proverbial brick wall.' She pushed her long dark hair back behind her ears and said, 'Anyway, sit down, Jenny. What's the favour?'

I told her about the old people's party and my difficulty each year in finding enough helpers. 'And I just wondered . . .'

'I might have known I couldn't keep it a secret!' Helen laughed. 'You know, don't you? About Christmas at Brecondale?'

'Yes. Matron told Charles you were a godsend. How did you know they needed help?'

'Easy. They put a poster up in the clinic. I thought there'd be lots of other volunteers, but there was only me.'

'And Sophie!' I reminded her.

As if on cue, Helen's miniature padded in from the adjoining bedroom and climbed on to her mother's knee.

Helen kissed the dark fringe. 'Hello, nosey. That was a short nap. Did you hear Aunty Jenny?'

Sophie beamed at me and blinked twice.

Helen said, 'I'd have to bring Sophie, though. Would that be OK?'

'Of course you must bring her. She'll be part of the entertainment, charming her way from lap to lap!'

'And what else have you got on the programme, other

than the delectable Miss Sophie Waites?'

'Well, Moth's going to see someone at the library who does the archives. Apparently, they've recently put hundreds of old photographs of our locality on to transparencies for reference and cataloguing or something. Moth thinks they'd make a splendid trip down memory lane for the Senior Citizens. You'll come, then? Thursday?'

'We'll come,' Helen promised, and I went home to fix some lunch.

Thursday came, cold but bright, which augured well for a good turn out of 'fit and mobiles' — those older people still able to make their own way to church or wherever.

At ten to three I left Helen and two of the Ladies' Guild putting the finishing touches to the decorated tea-tables while Moth and I took the minibus and the car to Brecondale to pick up the 'halt and the lame'. Moth carefully arranged an assorted dozen in the bus, plus zimmers, sticks, rugs and handbags, and I settled three elderly ladies in the car.

'Where's the vicar, then? Last year, the vicar fetched us!' Old people can be very blunt.

'I'm sorry, Mrs Knowles. He's doing a service at the crematorium. But he'll be popping in to our party when he gets back.'

'How'll he *get* back? I mean, if *you've* got his car?'

It's not *his* car. It's *our* car. But I didn't press the point. 'Oh, I expect the undertaker will drop him off.'

Mrs Knowles was one reason why I had problems finding willing volunteers for the Senior Citizens' party. Deaf to the tuts and shushes of her colleagues she went on, 'Well, I don't think that's right. The vicar turning up at a pensioners' party in a hearse. Looks like he's expecting some business. As if he won't get us soon enough anyway.'

46

Miss McIlroy and Mrs Keene stared at their gloved hands.

'Hearse indeed!' hissed Mrs Knowles, unwilling to let it drop.

'I rather think, Mrs Knowles, that he'll be in the chief mourners' limousine,' I said, more out of irritation than conviction. Charles often comes home in the hearse.

I braked a mite too sharply at the church hall gates, pursing my lips against smiling as Mrs Knowles's over-large fur hat settled heavily on her glasses. A small but sweet come-uppance I'd think about repenting of some other time!

We've long since learned not to postpone serving tea at this function. In the old days, when we put on the entertainment before the meal, the guests got more and more restless and less and less interested in the singers and magicians. Even when we changed the timetable, sitting them down to eat on arrival at three o'clock, they fell on the food with a ferocity that betrayed some prudent prior fasting. I couldn't blame them, really. I mean, if you're going out to an ample free tea, why bother with lunch?

As I circulated with the giant tea-pot, I was aware of Mrs Knowles's strident voice above the general chatter and the carols from the cassette-player. 'Fancy giving us all this stodge!' she was complaining, while piling her plate with enough cakes and sandwiches to see her through to Easter. 'I suppose you realize this could cause a serious blockage in the alimentary canal?'

Poor Mr Emerson nearly had hot tea poured all over his slippers while I blinked at such biological sophistication. He'd heard it, too. Or at least, half-heard it.

'They're all the same,' he said, ruefully shaking his

head. 'All them old canals. They were bound to block up once the barges stopped running.'

Moth, handing out paper hats and Christmas crackers, came to my rescue. 'I hear they're clearing them now, Mr Emerson. Opening them up for holiday boats. Actually, my brother's taking a canal holiday this year. Now, what d'you think — red hat? Green?'

The crackers brought a surge of snaps, laughs and whistles, then as we went round with the trifle, I heard Mrs Knowles again.

'Martyr to it, I am, dear.' She was talking to Helen. 'Yes, a *martyr* to constipation, that's what I am. I go for weeks without going, if you understand me, and I spend hours and hours in the lavatory, all to no avail!'

Helen smiled nervously and I heard her ask, 'Er — don't you, er, take anything?'

And while Mrs Knowles drew breath for a lecture on the perils of laxatives, little Miss McIlroy jumped in with, 'Aye, she takes her knitting!'

The 'martyr' turned a nasty puce colour which clashed with the red paper crown, but her sniping opponent was saved from a faceful of trifle (or worse) by the sudden appearance of baby Sophie at Mrs Knowles' knee. With a rhythmical bang of the spoon on the eye-level kneecap she pleaded, 'Up! Up! Pudding!'

'Oh Lord,' I prayed silently from the next table, 'please don't let her take it out on the child. *I* can handle the old bissom, but Sophie's only a baby.' I was forgetting, of course, that Sophie had a lot more going for her than I had. A cherubic face, sweet trusting eyes peeping out from under her thick fringe, and oodles and oodles of charm.

The change in Mrs Knowles was nothing short of miraculous.

'Well, look who's here. It's the little angel from our Christmas tree, isn't it, pet?' And she helped Sophie to scramble on to her lap and proceeded to share her own large dish of trifle, joking in baby-talk between each precarious spoonful. 'Now, where shall we put the red jelly-welly? Open wide! No — not up your nosey-wosey. Oh dear. Aunty Knowles wipe it off. There!'

'Aunty' Knowles had at last found someone who readily accepted her wisdom and guidance, albeit as part of the pudding.

As soon as the tables were cleared, Moth switched on the slide-projector.

'No, keep the lights on for a minute while I explain. Ladies and gentlemen! I've managed to borrow some old photographs from the library. But I'll need your help in identifying them, because of course I'm the new boy round here. OK, let's see what we've got, shall we? Lights out!'

Even Moth knew the first picture. Our church, St Cuthbert's, in sepia tint, with neat clipped shrubs and fancy iron railings on the boundary wall. They're not there now. I suppose they went for the war effort.

We moved on to slide number two. 'Now, who's this?'

'Canon Coldshaw' came the chorus in recognition of the stern, white-haired gentleman with a very wide dog-collar.

Heavens! Water in the boating lake in Albert Park! These days it's a dumping-hole for chip papers and beer cans. Someone spotted the Bickershaw brothers with a model yacht. That would be George and the brother who was killed at Ypres. George Bickershaw was churchwarden when we first arrived in the parish, but he died some time ago.

'Remember the open-topped trams? But which street is it?'

'Mill Street!'

'No, Marsh Street! There's the Maypole Dairy where I worked before the war!'

Which war, I wondered?

Moth's slides were marvellous entertainment for these people. Some of them might have difficulty remembering their room number at Brecondale, but they could recall every brick in the parish of sixty years ago.

'I think I know this next one,' said Moth. 'It's the crossroads where the video library is now.'

I studied the scene with particular interest. Helen lived over the Video Exchange.

'The Pie Shop!'

'Knowles's Pie Shop!'

What? I looked carefully at the name above the old emporium where the white-aproned owner stood in the doorway with his arms folded. Yes. It was Knowles, all right. 'Beef Pies, J. C. Knowles, Pork Pies', said the legend.

'I've got that one at home,' announced Mrs Knowles. 'That's my Harold's father. We lived over that shop, me and Harold, before we bought the bungalow. Then we let it off and just kept the shop. And when Harold retired we let the shop as well. Prams and cycles, they sold. Remember?' There were lots of 'ayes' and nods. 'And now it's that I-don't-know-what. Video, is it? I suppose they still pay rent. Only Mr Hancock does all that now.'

Williams and Hancock. Of course! The estate agents who collected Helen's rent. And now we knew who her landlord was. Or rather, landlady.

Charles crept in while we were picking out old familiar faces lined up alongside an ancient fire-engine.

'I'll do the return run to Brecondale,' he offered. But I now had a reason to take Mrs Knowles home myself. I'd see her up to her room, I decided, then broach the subject of Helen's flat.

But Mrs Knowles beat me to it. When the other ladies in the car enthused about the wonderful time they'd had, she sniffed. 'Not my kind of meal, of course. And that Ladies' Guild *always* let the tea stew. But the young one's nice enough. That Helen. She lives in my old apartment, you know. Isn't that lovely?' Before any of us could venture an opinion, she went on loftily, 'Actually, I'm invited there for tea on Sunday. She says I remind her of her own dear grandmother. And you saw how little Sophie's taken to me, didn't you?' Again, we made no comment. I just drove. Miss McIlroy and Mrs Keene gazed out of the windows into the darkness. 'So I've had a word with the curate, and he's going to pick me up. Of course, he'll be having tea with us, too.'

I'd already guessed I wasn't Mrs Knowles' favourite chauffeur (or chauffeuse). But Moth? Having tea with Helen? What a lovely thought! My mind was working overtime as we pulled up outside Brecondale. We nearly overshot the main entrance, so I'm quite prepared to accept that I may have braked hastily again, though quite unintentionally this time. Certainly, any driver who makes your hat lurch forward with enough thrust to shoot your glasses on to the floor *is* open to criticism, I suppose.

Poor Matron didn't know what to make of the response to her query, 'Had a lovely time, then, ladies?'

Mrs Knowles checked that she still had four limbs, a hat and a handbag, and then she said icily, 'We'd have been better off in the hearse.'

But I thought that, all in all, it had been quite a promising afternoon!

51

6 February

❋ My Sooty Valentine

When he was arranging the assortment of supposedly character-building irritations commonly known as 'things that are sent to try us', the Almighty hit on a winning combination for February. From his point of view, at least. From *my* point of view, it seemed more likely that some malevolent pagan gods had contrived to combine sudden frost on top of slushy snow; the boys' half-term; a Shrove Tuesday (plus obligatory social) on the eve of St Valentine's Day; and a decision by the committee to ditch the usual barn dance in favour of a Pop-Hop with disco and band. Oh boy, *was* I being tried!

I suppose slipping on the drive on my way back from the shops was about par for the course. I lumbered into the kitchen with a grazed knee, torn tights, and a broken jar of piccallili dripping its contents through the nylon netting of my shopping bag. However, my entrance caused but a minor stir in the chaos inside. Only the steamy warmth was welcoming.

Joshua was kneeling in the middle of the table surrounded by jagged pieces of metal. He was wielding a pair of over-large tin shears very inexpertly.

'Hi, Mum. What time's tea?'

I ignored him.

Drew had shoved some books and my ironing to one end of the work surface to make room for the fizzy drinks machine we'd bought them for Christmas. He seemed to be engaged in discovering how ear-splittingly high he could make the gas cylinder whistle without actually bursting the bottle of frenzied water.

'Close the door, Mum,' he shouted. 'It's cold!'

I was going to kick the door anyway, so I did. Then I limped to the sink, dumped my shopping bag in it, and dabbed at my knee with the dishcloth.

'What happened to *you*?' Drew shouted again, above the gassy scream.

I erupted. 'Stop playing with that thing!' I yelled at him. 'It'll . . . explode!'

The whistle became a gentle hiss and vanished.

'I fell on the ice,' I said in the quiet.

From his vantage point on the table, Josh looked down at my shoes. 'You're bleeding yellow. Isn't that strange? Do you think your blood is, you know, jaundiced?'

'It's piccallili!' I snapped.

Drew stopped swigging at his bottle of fizz and wiped his mouth with the back of his hand. 'Even stranger, then. Veins flowing with mustard pickle. Have you told the BMA?'

'Oh, for pity's sake, you two! Why aren't you in the church hall? You said you'd help with the dance decorations.'

'They didn't want us.'

'We got thrown out for larking.'

'Well, if you want any tea, you'll have to clear out of here, too. And take all your rubbish with you.' My eyes caught the books at Drew's elbow. 'Are those your books, Drew? How many times have I told you not to do your homework in the kitchen. They'll get grease and jam and heaven knows what on them.'

'Yes. Blood and piccallili. Anyway, they're not mine. They're Moth's.'

'Well, take them up to the flat, would you?'

Suddenly, my eyes were hooked by the word 'tea-time' as it flashed at me from the piece of blue metal wriggling about in Josh's tin-shears.

'*Josh*!' I shrieked. 'What *are* you cutting up? It's my best cake-tin!'

'No it's not, Mum. It said somebody's tea-time assorted biscuits.'

'That one *is* my best cake-tin. It's airtight!' The farcical inappropriateness of the present tense was not lost on us as we both surveyed the mangled shreds littered round his knees.

'How was I to know? It was empty.'

I sighed. Saturday's bake just about sees Sunday's tea. *All* the tins are empty by Tuesday.

I turned to rescue my shopping from the messy bag in the sink. 'What are you making, anyway?'

'It's a secret. I'll show you when it's finished.'

'Well, would you mind finishing it somewhere else? I need the table.'

Josh jumped down and carefully collected the lethal pieces, while I dumped the burst pickle jar and the shopping bag in the kitchen bin.

'Where's your father? Church hall?'

Josh paused with his bottom against the swing door, ready to push. 'No. I think he said he was going to, er, "lay hands" on the church boiler.'

Like father, like son. Born tinkerers, the two of them.

'I wish he wouldn't,' I said. 'I'm sure he hasn't the foggiest idea what he's doing.' But Josh was gone, and I was left talking to the door swinging behind him.

The kitchen was suddenly empty and still. They'd have left me alone even if I hadn't banished them, poor things. I wasn't very good company in this kind of mood. There *are* days when I wish I'd married a road sweeper or an airline pilot or a burglar, or anyone at all who wasn't a vicar. And this was one of them.

I looked at the clock and took stock of the situation. The casserole was in the oven. Just the wretched pancakes for dessert. I had time for a cup of tea and a sit before attacking the flour, milk and eggs. While I waited for the kettle, I peered closely at my reflection in the chrome trim on the splashback of the cooker. What was the matter with me? Apart from the tired perm and the crow's feet?

The tea revived my brain and cleared my thoughts. Expectations. That was the trouble. People had expectations of me, just because I was the vicar's wife.

My grazed knee throbbed, as if to remind me that the weather could hardly be blamed on my husband's profession. No, it was Rita, Rita MacDonald. Rita who ran the playgroup. Not just ran it, revelled in it. Rita, who delighted in boxes full of Lego, full of Playdough. Rita, who sang as she mopped up all the accidents just outside the ladies' toilets. Rita, who was without a doubt the best playgroup leader for miles around.

Now, why should I be grumpy about Rita, I wondered? Was I jealous of her capabilities in an area where I'd be all at sea? No. Each to his own. I knew I was big enough to let other people shine in their own particular callings even when I felt singularly tarnished in mine. I'd be seeing Rita later at the dance and . . . drat! That was it. Deep down, I was dreading seeing Rita Macdonald because of something she'd said after church on Sunday.

'Ever such a demand for facilities for even younger toddlers.' I could remember quite clearly now. 'Plenty of space in the church hall. But I'd need extra help. Would you give it some thought?'

For two days I'd pushed it as far as I could from my thoughts, for two reasons. One, I couldn't have been less enthusiastic about helping with babies and nappies. All that kind of thing seems so remote when your own are so big. And two, I heartily resented the assumption that I wouldn't be so churlish as to refuse. After all, wasn't I the vicar's wife?

The vicar's wife!

'Dear God, sometimes I think it's *hell* being the vicar's wife!'

I spoke aloud, and for a split second I thought I'd incurred instant retribution from above. An enormous bang shook the floor beneath my chair and rattled the windowsill plants in their saucers.

'*The boiler*!' I ran out into the dusk and raced across the crunchy grass to the back of the church.

'Charles! Charles! Oh God, I didn't mean it. Let him be all right, *please*!'

He *was* all right. He was sitting in the little snowdrift at the foot of the boiler room steps, between the boiler room door and the hole where the boiler room door should have been, panting heavily and trying to laugh. Nerves, of course.

I slithered down the icy stairway. 'Darling, are you all right? Don't move.'

He looked up, managed a smile, and the face was a still from a hundred comedy classics. Totally blackened, right into his hair, so his teeth and his eyes were *too* white. He obliged with a Stan Laurel blink, then the eyes creased into their usual blue twinkle.

'Just winded, Jen, really. It blew up.'

Moth appeared from nowhere and supported Charles as he staggered up the steps to the garden. A quick check confirmed that no bones were broken.

'Come on,' said Moth. 'A bit of a rest and a cup of tea would probably not go amiss. And I'll call the doctor.'

But Charles said no to the doctor. And I must say, by the time he'd cleaned up and was resting on our bed in his dressing-gown, he looked almost normal. Almost.

'Yes, I prefer you without the soot,' I told him, 'but I do miss the eyelashes. Your brows are very thin, too, aren't they?'

Charles grinned. 'Oh, they'll grow, don't you worry. I'm just glad nothing hit me, only the heat. Jolly lucky, you know, Jenny. There were bits of boiler flying everywhere.'

'Moth says there must have been a blockage in one of the water pipes,' I told him. 'Perhaps now Drew will stop messing about with that fizzy drinks cylinder!'

Charles put his teacup on the bedside table and took hold of my hand.

'Come here,' he said, and pulled me to sit beside him. 'I'm sorry I scared you, Jenny. I wouldn't hurt you for the world. I shouldn't have meddled with something I know nothing about. Forgive me?'

'Of course I forgive you, silly. I'm just so relieved you're alive!'

'I love you, Jen.'

'I love you, too,' I said, and I kissed one frazzled eyebrow.

It was a tender moment and I decided to capitalize on it. 'Actually, darling, I peeped at the Valentine card. It's beautiful.'

Charles looked puzzled.

'Oh, don't be cross,' I pleaded. 'I found it just now in the kitchen. I didn't open it deliberately, only I didn't know what it was so I pulled it out to see. But I've put it back, so you can give it me properly tomorrow.'

Charles bit his lip. 'Jenny, sweetest. I hardly know how to say this after scaring you half to death, but I — er — didn't buy you a card. I'm afraid I forgot.'

'But Charles,' I protested, 'it's lovely! And the verse! I mean, it's not the sort of thing the boys would . . .'

It took just the slightest pause for the same thought to strike us both. Moth and Helen?

'You know, Jenny, I think we're going to see quite a lot of young Helen if Moth's got anything to do with it.'

'Suits me!' I said, and I meant it.

'In fact,' Charles said, 'Rita MacDonald phoned me this morning to say Helen has offered to help with the new Mums and Toddlers group. I was supposed to tell you.'

I sighed. Relief *and* remorse. What on earth had I got so wound up for? Of course Rita wouldn't pressure me with psychological blackmail. She wouldn't know how, bless her. She'd meant me to suggest someone suitable. Someone like Helen. Certainly not myself.

I felt pretty bad, but Charles went on. 'And she also said that Moth's going to pick up all the extra equipment they've been offered. And something else. What was it? Oh yes, had I heard the latest name for Mums' and Toddlers' groups?'

'I don't think *I* have. What is it?'

'Squeals on wheels!'

I laughed and picked up his empty cup.

'Talking of, er — meals . . . are you coming down to eat with us?'

'No. I think I'll conserve my strength for later. The least I can do is waltz with my wife when I forgot to buy her a Valentine.'

Waltz? There was something my husband obviously didn't know.

'Charles, darling, the band have all got green and pink hair and masonry nails in their ears. But if you want to waltz, then we'll waltz!'

I found a lovely surprise waiting for me in the kitchen.

The boys had got the meal ready, including mixing and cooking the dreaded pancakes. After the lamb casserole, they brought the dessert to the table with a flourish and a fanfare. I couldn't believe my eyes. *Heart-shaped pancakes*!

'How did you *do* it?'

'With your new present!' Josh beamed, with obvious pride.

'You know, Mum. The one he was making this afternoon.'

Josh lifted a large metal pastry-cutter sort of thing from the frying-pan. A perfect heart.

'See?' he said, 'I made it. Out of your very best cake-tin!'

Love comes in many guises. Like one slightly singed vicar waltzing romantically with one middle aged lady with a limp, to the thunderous pulse of the week's number one song, 'After the Bomb'!

7 March

❉ It's an Ill Wind . . .

Poor St Cuthbert. I doubt if he ever had such a miserable patronal festival as we gave him on March 20th. And poor Moth. For weeks his PH D thesis had played second fiddle to the church public address system, which he was re-jigging to include some recorded bells that could be broadcast from the tower. (The timbers supporting the original peal were declared unsafe after the last war and the real bells haven't been rung since.)

He was so keen, bless him. 'Won't it be lovely?' he enthused. 'Bells ringing out all over the parish again on our St Cuthbert's Day!'

I don't know what went wrong with Moth's wiring. I don't think he does. I stood outside for ages with Josh and Drew before the special service, waiting for the bells to start. All we got was an occasional hiss that was in any case lost in the wind.

And then, when Charles got up into the pulpit to preach, the microphone wasn't working either. Well, not properly. Instead of his voice coming to us out of the speakers on the window ledges, it seemed to be emerging from somewhere in the roof. It was really quite spooky and largely unintelligible.

I'm not sure whether it counts as a tragedy or a blessing that there were so few of us in church to hear him anyway. Knowing what he'd be up against, Charles had tried over the previous weeks to jolly his congregation into unswerving attendance, particularly for the patronal festival.

'Why,' he'd insisted expansively, 'living all his life in the north-east, as he did, dear St Cuthbert could even qualify as patron saint of all this inclement weather!'

All to no avail. In the event, the awful cold dissuaded most of our folk from coming to celebrate our name-saint's day.

Not that they could be blamed. Vast Victorian churches are never warm. A vast Victorian church with a broken boiler and no heating is very cold in March, especially after the thawing February snow reveals lead flashing to be missing from the roof, leaving us with extra damp walls. And in a particularly windy March, a damp, unheated vast Victorian church whose windows have also suffered at the hands of the local vandals can produce draughts that could threaten Siberia.

So it was a fairly dispirited if faithful few who turned up, appropriately lagged, on our saint's day. But we ran up the flag on the tower anyway, to let Cuthbert know that despite the depression he wasn't forgotten. And there was a bright spot in the service itself, during Charles' sermon, when Moth disappeared behind the pulpit to joggle the knobs on his newly adapted amplifier. He didn't actually manage to get Charles's microphone working for us, but he did get the electronic bells going. *Inside* church! Halfway through Charles's second point! For a deafening split second they bonged at us from the speakers on the window ledges, leaving us all with ringing in our ears long after the mortified curate had crawled back to his stall, his normally pale face so reddened, I thought his blond hair would turn pink.

A good part of Moth's discomfiture was due to the fact that he knew what we didn't, just then, although it was the talk of the parish for weeks afterwards. That the reason Charles's voice wasn't coming to us through the church speakers was because a crossed wire had sent it booming out across the parish from the tower, like some Orwellian 'Big Brother'. Fortunately, the noise of the wind made Charles's very public address slightly less conspicuous than it might have been, but guilty parishioners for several streets around insisted for ages that the vicar had gone too far this time.

Not that Charles was unduly worried. I think he saw it all as a huge joke. Certainly, he was his normal cheery self when he left for the crematorium the next day.

'Bye, love!' he shouted from the hall. 'I should be back by eleven, but if I'm not, keep him talking.'

'Keep who talking?'

'The press photographer. Bye.'

Press photographer? Charles hadn't mentioned him before, but I wasn't all that surprised. A local paper had featured our battle against vandalism and one or two of the national dailies had latched on to it.

I was busy in the kitchen when the doorbell rang. 'Drat! Still in my housecoat.' Some mornings I win, some I don't. Then the phone started ringing, too.

I opened the door hurriedly and said to the man on the doorstep, 'Do come in. My husband will be here any minute to help with the photographs. Can you just hang on a moment while I answer that phone?'

He looked a bit puzzled, but the phone was insistent.

'Good morning. St Cuthbert's vicarage.'

'Oh, Jenny, you are in. Good. For a minute there I thought you'd gone out. It seems ages since I saw you. Now, I know I said I'd come to that thing last night, but what with all this wind and my bad chest, you know. Anyway, I thought I'd phone you instead for a nice long chat. Did Elsie tell you I'd seen her? She said . . .'

'Er . . . Alice. Can I ring you back? There's someone at the door.'

'Really, dear? I didn't hear the doorbell.'

'Well, no. It went before you rang.'

'I see. All right, then. If that's how it is.'

'No, Alice, don't be silly, it's . . .'

'Goodbye!'

I sighed and went back to the photographer. 'I'm sorry to keep you waiting. My husband's out at a funeral, but he's due back any time now.'

'Actually, Mrs . . . erm . . . I've only come to read the electric.'

Heavens! I apologized, showed him the vicarage meter, then gave him the keys for the church and church hall.

The doorbell rang again. This time it *was* the press photographer, a very good-looking but extremely shy young man.

'Please come in. No, you're not late! As a matter of fact, my husband's not back from a funeral, but he won't be very long now.'

I hoped!

I closed the garden door after the electric man and turned to ask the photographer if he'd like some coffee. He was still standing in the draughty porch, and seemed disinclined to venture further. Presumably it was my housecoat.

'Oh, let's wait in the sitting room,' I said. 'It's very much cosier in there.'

I suppose it depends what you mean by cosy. I hadn't actually been in the sitting room that morning, so when I swung open the door and ushered him in ahead of me, the poor fellow stepped into the intimate semi-darkness of curtains drawn against the daylight. In my haste to dash past him to open them, I tripped over a stool in the gloom and knocked the photographer on to the sofa with what can only be described as an over-amorous rugby tackle. Trying not to notice his crimson-faced alarm, I leapt ten feet into the air, whizzed open the curtains and dashed out for the coffee.

When I came back with the tray, I saw the electric man just beyond the sitting room window as he crossed the garden on his way back from the church. The next moment, there was an almighty crash upstairs, with the breaking of glass, and a blood-curdling howl from outside.

The young photographer froze in terror, his eyes bulging, as he doubtless quaked at the further awful tortures I unleashed on innocent male visitors! Actually, it was just as well I'm not of a nervous disposition, I might have jumped on his knee in terror. Instead, I smiled carefully and said, 'Would you excuse me? Something appears to be happening.'

In the hall, I met the electric man, quivering with shock. 'It's your window, missus! Upstairs window!' he panted. 'Wind's got it. Missed me by inches, it did!'

He refused my offer of a cup of sweet coffee and fled to the normality of the house next door. I went to inspect the damage. In Joshua's bedroom, what remained of the casement window-frame was crashing itself to pieces on the outside wall.

I heard Charles call, 'Hello. I'm back.'

At last! I dashed downstairs to the hall and grabbed him even before he could pull off his robes, but he got in first with, 'Who was that fellow flying down the front path?'

'That,' I said, 'was the electric man. I think *he* thinks I tried to guillotine him. Your photographer's in the sitting room. *He* thinks I tried to seduce him! A window's blown out upstairs, and that banging you can hear is the frame bashing itself to bits. And now,' I announced, with a finality that obviously puzzled him as much as all the news, 'I'm just going to lock myself in the upstairs loo with my library book. I might come out at lunchtime if it's definitely all clear.'

By the time we sat down together for our soup and cheese, Charles had had his picture taken against a background of suitably 'holey' windows; he'd lashed the remains of Josh's window-frame back in its proper place, nailed a piece of hardboard to it, and arranged for a local builder to come round and take a look. And I'd read several chapters of escapist romantic fiction. Mental chewing-gum or love-by-the-yard or whatever, but at least I was human again.

Life seemed quite normal by the time the builder had measured Josh's window. Then as he jotted down the vital statistics on a scrap of paper with his chisel-shaped pencil, he asked, 'By the way, who's died?'

I shrugged and looked at Charles.

'Do you mean Miss Robertson? Retired laundry manageress from Hardcastle Street? I did her funeral this morning at the crematorium.'

'Famous, was she?' pursued the builder. 'Sort of local dignitary or something?'

'Not that I'm aware of,' Charles confessed. 'Nice enough old dear, but not in any sense a public figure. Why do you ask?'

'Oh, just wondered. Only your flag's at half-mast, see.'

It was, too. When Charles went up the tower to check why it had slipped, he found the wind had made an incredible tangle of the rope.

'Heaven preserve us!' he shivered over the tea I made to warm him again. 'Honestly, Jenny, it's like the summit of Everest up there! No way I could shift that flag, though.

Rope's all knotted up round the pulley. Couldn't even wrench the wretched thing down, so it'll probably be shredded to pieces before tomorrow.'

However, as things turned out, the church flag was totally forgotten by the morrow. As the five of us gathered for breakfast, it was the tale of 'Moth's Exciting Night' that was top of the bill.

'What *I* want to know,' said Drew, 'is what on earth you were doing in church at *three o'clock in the morning*?'

'Yes,' Josh followed. 'Have you gone like the old monks, Moth? You know, prayers every hour through the night?'

'Fat chance!' Moth yawned. 'I like my bed too much for that. Only last night as it happened I couldn't sleep. Partly the noise of the wind, and partly wondering about why my sound wiring didn't work.' He stirred his muesli thoughtfully, still pondering the problem.

'So?' Charles encouraged his curate with a buttery knife.

'So I decided to get dressed and check it all through once more.'

'And you bumped into a man in a mask and a striped shirt, with a bag over his shoulder marked "SWAG"!'

Drew ducked Charles's attempted cuff round the ear.

'Get on with your toast and let Moth tell it or you'll finish up late for school.'

'Yes, Moth,' I urged as I poured the tea, 'go on, do. I'm all ears.'

I watched as Josh deliberately decided not to comment, and Moth continued his tale.

'I took my car inspection lamp to work by', he said, 'rather than switch the church lights on. So I suppose from outside you wouldn't even know I was in there. Anyway, I was looking at the cable that goes from the tape-machine to the amp., and I suddenly noticed how strong the wind was. It seemed to be lifting the roof slates. But when I listened hard, it was more of a scraping noise. Well, I suppose it could have been anything, but it did occur to me that someone might have come back for the rest of the lead flashing. The only thing was, I was far too scared to go out and look in case there was a gang of them!'

'Dead right,' Josh nodded. 'Imagine being hit over the head with a bagful of lead gutter. *Pow*!'

'So I thought, if there *is* someone on the roof, how can I stop them pinching what's left of our lead? Then I saw the cable I'd pinned to the wall and it gave me an idea. You know, the wire that goes from the amp. to the speaker in the tower.'

It was delicious! We all nodded, 'Go on, go on.'

'I switched the amp. on, went up into the pulpit and preached a very short, very loud sermon!'

'Yahoo!'

'Fantastic!'

'And then I ran into the vestry and dialled 999.'

Charles caught his breath between bouts of laughter. 'What did you say?'

'What, on the phone?'

'No, down the microphone.'

'The first thing that came into my head. "Be sure your sins will find you out!"'

'No wonder he went quietly. You probably deafened him for life!'

'Oh, I expect he'll recover,' Moth smiled. 'In fact, the police said they thought his conscience was giving him more trouble than his ears. He'd really thought it was the Almighty for a minute!'

'And he confessed to another six roofs, you say?'

'Apparently. I'd have woken you up, you know, Charles,

only as my sermon obviously hadn't roused you I thought it a shame to disturb you. Anyway, the police are calling in to see you sometime this morning.'

Suddenly I noticed the clock. 'School! Come on, you two. And brush your teeth before you go! And close the front door when you leave. There's an awful draught if you don't.'

Charles folded his arms and tilted back slightly in his chair. 'Do you know,' he said, 'I thought that vestry phone was a waste? I was going to have it removed. Good job I didn't, eh?'

Josh's head suddenly appeared round the swing door.

'Dad! The flag's changed corners! Come and look!'

We all trooped out on to the front drive. It was quite amazing, really. Somehow, the wind had finally whipped our flag off its official flag-pole, which is attached to one of the tower's four pinnacles, and had wrapped it round the weather cock, attached to an adjacent pinnacle.

'Good Heavens! How'll I sort that out? That mast's at least eight feet high!'

'Take a ladder up,' said Josh.

'Oh, great in this wind, idiot!' said Drew.

'For pity's sake, will you please *go to school*!' I yelled at both of them.

They shuffled off, and Moth said to Charles, 'D'you know, I'd leave it. It's still fluttering cheerfully enough. And I rather think Cuthbert deserves an extra few days' celebration after the mess I made of his service.'

Charles rubbed his arms to keep warm as he watched the tattered flag cracking from the weather vane. 'Well, I'll say this, Moth: I bet he's never had a more *memorable* patronal festival.'

'Please can we go in, now?' I begged between chattering teeth. 'Fancy a fresh pot of tea?'

8 April

✤ A Slow Boat to . . . Heaven

I'm still not sure how I let Moth talk us into it. The canal holiday, I mean.

We all knew *he* was going off on a narrow boat for his post-Easter break. His brother Tom had invited him soon after Christmas when he was making the booking for his own family. Then I gradually became aware of references to Helen and Sophie. It was nice to think of them getting a proper holiday, and I knew Tom and Meg would love them as we did. And that young Justin and Lisa would be delighted with little Sophie as a playmate.

Then sometime well into Lent, I came across Moth and Charles in the kitchen poring over a glossy brochure.

'Look, this one.' Moth was jabbing at a drawing. 'See. Ten actual bed spaces, plus two canvas stretcher things. It sleeps twelve, and we'd only be eleven.'

Charles seemed doubtful. 'Yes, but can you sleep in family units? There'd be two married couples, plus two single adults and five assorted children. How would it work?'

Moth smiled up at him. 'Simple,' he said. 'There are doors all over the place that fasten across at night to section the boat into cabins. So you get double bunks in that cabin, and that one, and that one.' The long ecclesiastical finger hopped around the page. 'And the two dining-areas become double beds.'

Charles nodded as comprehension settled. 'And where are the stretcher things? Are they just child-sized?'

'Oh no. They'll take adults. You're just a bit near the ceiling, that's all. They clip on to brackets between that wardrobe and the shower, and between the galley (that's the kitchen) and that loo.'

Charles sniffed. 'OK. So how does it work in detail?'

By this time I'd abandoned the dishes on the draining board and was standing over the two men with my arms folded round the tea-towel. It was quite fascinating, this plan of a narrow boat interior. It looked like a very long caravan with a pointed front. Sort of gothic window shape.

'Well,' said Moth, 'I think what Tom reckoned was this. Helen and Sophie in a cabin with bunks, Justin and Lisa in a cabin with bunks, Tom and Meg on a dining-area double, and me on one of the stretchers. That leaves the other dining-area and a set of bunks for all of you.'

I was smiling and nodding at the logic of it when the penny dropped.

'*Us?*' I yelled, and they both looked round, Moth a golden glow of enthusiasm behind his gilt specs and blond hair; Charles with his dark and devilish grin.

'Yes, us, Jenny. Tom wants us to go as his guests.'

I tried to resist. I reminded Charles about a clergy wife we know who had to be fished out of a lock. It took the bishop to dissuade her from divorcing her bargee-husband.

'That was different,' said Charles. 'They were doing it all without help. With three strapping men and all the kids, you women won't have to worry about the lock-gates.'

'No,' said Moth. 'You can sit on the roof and sun yourselves, and watch the cows grazing, and the willows brushing the water, while we chug along gently at four miles an hour.' It sounded idyllic.

So, Easter Monday saw our contingent piling out of the

church minibus at a canalside boatyard deep in the country. I spotted Tom's Range Rover and wondered how on earth ordinary mortals managed with family saloon cars at times like this. We'd brought enough luggage for a world cruise.

'Welcome aboard!' Tom was waving from the long blue boat tied up by the towpath, and once all the reunions and introductions were over, we formed a human chain to transfer our cargo.

Honestly, we had so much stuff, I'm sure anyone watching must have thought the boat-owner would never see his 'Mellingworth Castle' again. Boxes and boxes of food, dozens of bin-bags stuffed with clothes. ('Bring all your woollies,' Meg had said on the phone, 'and we use plastic bags because there's nowhere to stow suitcases.') Enough waterproof gear to furnish a polar expedition, and hundreds of assorted wellie-boots. But the sun was shining, there were primroses along the front of the boatyard office and I looked forward to unpacking my shorts and relaxing on the roof with a good book.

'We're quite settled in,' said Meg. 'Been for a short trip already. But then, we didn't have to come as far as you. We thought Helen and Sophie at the end near the loo, then our two, then your two next to Moth. You can have this dining-area here — the table drops to make a bed — and we're up in that one.'

I was marvelling at how well equipped our temporary home was, from big fridge to racks of wineglasses, when Meg lifted a cushioned seat in 'her' dining-area.

'Clothes and bedding go under here, see. It's very roomy and . . . AAGH!'

I ran to look. 'What is it? What's in there?'

'It's all *wet*! Look at the children's clothes. They're soaked through!' She lifted out a small greenish-grey white vest and held it dripping over the hole while her face wondered whether to laugh or to cry.

Helen was on the towpath fitting the children out with life-jackets amid gales of laughter, but the men heard Meg's scream and came clattering down below from the open cockpit at the back of the boat.

'Bilge!' was Tom's verdict when he'd inspected the disaster area.

'My feelings precisely,' wailed Meg in response.

'No, I mean that's what it is. The pump's obviously faulty. Should be shoving it back into the canal, but apparently it isn't, if it's got to this level.'

'I'll get the owner,' Moth offered.

But Tom stopped him. 'No use. He's gone. All his other hire people came and went on Saturday and he only came down today to see us in. He left just before you arrived.'

'Well, what do I do, Tom?' Meg was getting desperate. 'Our stuff's still in the bin-bags, but I'd emptied the children's to get extra socks for Lisa's wellies. Every last stitch is awash!'

It seemed like tears were about to win, so I grabbed the washing-up bowl from the sink and suggested some positive action instead.

'Come on, Meg. Let's wring them all out and wash them through by hand. They'll dry in no time on these radiators.'

So while the men took turns plunging their arms into the green slime under the weed hatch to sort out the bilge-pump, Meg and I washed pile upon pile of small garments in the galley sink, rinsed them under the shower and draped them all over the boat. The jet-set yacht image succumbed to water-gipsy muddle. But by the time we'd finished, the bilge-pump was doing its job properly, we'd got under way, and everyone felt better.

On holiday at last! I looked up from hanging a final pair

of knickers, to catch a glimpse of this four-miles-an-hour landscape Moth had raved about. All that the main window offered, however, was a screen of steamy condensation.

Well, it would be better from outside anyway, I thought, and I climbed the three steps to the open cockpit and pushed the little castle-painted doors.

'Hello, darling. Come on out, it's great.'

Charles was 'driving', one hand on the motor control, the other on the tiller. Tom and Moth were waiting to have a go, and I turned to look along the boat's almost endless roof to see Helen up at the front with all the children. My first thought was to go through the boat and rescue her, but I realized that my two were actually helping with the little ones, holding on to them and pointing at things in the fields as we rippled by. I knew Sophie had been tied to a line for extra safety. Everything was taken care of. I could relax.

I leaned my chin on my hands on the sliding roof above the steps where I stood, and let the breeze lift my hair. Oh, the open country after the dark winter months in the city. So fresh, so invigorating, so . . .

'Jen! I'm freezing! Fancy brewing up, darling?'

Back in the galley, I found Meg already pouring mugs of tea. 'You get used to it,' she said with old-timer's panache. 'Last time we did this, the kettle hardly cooled for a fortnight.'

When we'd fed and watered all hands, we tackled the steamy windows with kitchen tissue and liquid detergent and enjoyed our drink against the slowly changing panorama.

That first day was a bit bumpy while Charles learned how to get a long boat into a short lock without bashing everything in sight. But as all breakables were lashed down, including Sophie, no real damage was done. Josh and Drew soon got the hang of jumping off to open the lock-gates with the windlasses. They found bits of coloured paper in Justin's play-bag to make identification labels for these, because Tom had warned them about leaving the windlasses lying about after winding the lock paddles up or down, and neither of them wanted to be accused of losing his own and pinching his brother's.

By dusk that first night, even the adults could hardly wait to get to bed. The fresh air and the heavy lock-gates made us drowsy enough, but Tom's surprise at supper finished us off.

'Boxed wine is so easy to stow,' he said. 'It seemed silly not to bring some!'

But despite being completely bush-whacked, I didn't sleep well at all. The dining-table bed was comfy enough in our night-time private cabin, but we'd selected a shallow mooring place and the noise of the gravel on the boat bottom whenever the wind rocked us was unfamiliar enough to wake me several times.

Then Lisa woke and wanted her mummy. That meant trekking from her bunk at the front of the boat to her parents' double-bed diner at the back, via our cabin.

'Come on, sweetheart,' I whispered, as she padded through, wearing one of Tom's T-shirts — her fleecy nighty hadn't quite dried in time — 'Mummy's just through here, look.'

I'd just nodded off again when a very polite voice accosted my exposed ear. 'Aunty Jenny, my mummy's asleep. Which way did I come from?'

Charles, of course, slept like a lamb, even through my tossing and fretting.

By dawn, I knew I'd forgotten something in all the exhaustive packing. I should have brought the spare wax earplugs left in the packet after I'd tried them on Flossie for bonfire night. I determined to buy some more at the earliest opportunity. To this end, I spent the whole of Tuesday volunteering to go to the village shop every time we touched civilization.

Charles said I was probably having withdrawal symptoms after a day away from the city. Helen said Sophie would be splendidly tired after so many little walks with Aunty Jenny. Meg looked at all the stuff I'd felt obliged to buy at the few shops I did find, and said never mind, she'd make an enormous bread and butter pudding with gallons of milky custard for our evening dessert. She did, and it was lovely. And so filling, no one had room for the Edam cheese and biscuits.

We relaxed again over Tom's boxed wine, and I sleepily admired the shiny red cheese. Lovely red wine, and lovely red wax, I thought.

Wax? *Wax*!

It could have been manna from heaven! It was certainly an answer to prayer

Then, when the children were in bed and all the dishes put away, the adults sat around with the coffee while Charles read to us from Psalm 65:

> Thou visitest the earth and waterest it, thou greatly enrichest it . . . Thou waterest its furrows abundantly, settling its ridges, softening it with showers, and blessing its growth . . . The pastures of the wilderness drip, the hills gird themselves with joy, the meadows clothe themselves with flocks, the valleys deck themselves with grain, they shout and sing together with joy.

Tom and Meg retired first, followed by Charles and me.

'Sorry to throw you off your settee,' I said to Moth and Helen, 'but I think I'd like to turn in.'

'That's OK,' said Moth. 'We'll take a stroll along the

towpath. We'll come in the far end so as not to disturb you.'

'And we'll be very quiet,' said Helen.

I told them, 'Don't you worry,' secretly fingering the red wax in my pocket. 'I shan't hear a thing.'

I didn't either. But I did have scarlet-dyed ears all week.

Actually, it wasn't a week. It was six days, Monday to Saturday. Six days on another planet, light years away from the traffic of the city and the vicarage telephone. Six days of . . . well, friendship and fun, if not exactly peace.

It *was* fun watching the male contingent opening a lift-bridge contraption that worked by chains and weights. Tom, Charles and Moth pulled on the chains, and up tilted the little road-bridge.

'Hang on, Moth,' Charles said. 'Tom and I will bring her through.'

And hang on he did. As Tom and Charles jumped back on to the boat, the little road-bridge gently dropped down again across the canal to block our way, and Moth, still gripping the chain, rose slowly into the air like a Peter Pan. It took half-an-hour to negotiate that one bridge, while all the kids had a turn of being 'high and lifted up'.

It was Moth, too, who was first *in* the canal. But, to be fair, he didn't fall in. He went in voluntarily, after a pane of glass from the louvre-window in the shower plopped into the water when Drew, the driver, nudged a bridge. Out of consideration for the laundry-department, Moth stripped to his boxer shorts before lowering himself gingerly into the icy stillness. He found the glass panel, mercifully still intact. To the delight of the children he also found a rusty kettle, a bicycle wheel and a filthy lemonade bottle before we made him stop for fear of pneumonia or worse.

It was Josh who *fell* into the water. One beautiful sunny

morning he was mopping muddy boot-prints off the roof with rather too much gusto. His antics with the mop robbed him of his balance and he toppled in.

I think I was the only one who panicked. 'Quick! Get him Charles! He'll drown, he'll *drown*!'

'I doubt that. He's wearing a life-jacket and as far as I can see he's actually standing on the bottom anyway.'

Josh waded to the side of the boat. 'Sorry about that,' he said nonchalantly. 'Would somebody help me out?'

'Certainly,' said Charles. 'When you've been back for the mop.'

It wasn't all country cruising, of course. One night we moored in the suburbs of a large town, and the next morning we took the boat right into the town centre before breakfast so that Meg and I could shop for fresh bread and milk. The old forgotten canal meandered through, and under, tall department stores and office blocks. We crept along unnoticed in a grey spring drizzle, until Tom eventually tied up alongside some ancient stone steps, and Meg and I pulled on our waterproofs and wellies and climbed up to the main street.

It was only when we were at the checkout of the food department of Marks and Spencer's that we realized how strange our sou'westers and boots must have looked to the other shoppers.

'Heavens above!' said the till-girl as we approached with our money. 'Has the weather really got that bad since I came in?'

But then, that was the essence of the whole holiday; being part of another world entirely. Having fun and fellowship away from routines and deadlines. Having time to appreciate the Creator and his creation. A little bit of 'other-world' experience, to make us less than alien in Heaven.

Moth and Helen had a very heavenly week. We used the last of Tom's wine to toast them on our final evening aboard, when they shyly announced their engagement.

9 *May*

❊ Walking Day

'Helen, it's beautiful! I've never seen anything like it! Is it antique?'

Helen withdrew her hand in order to rescue Sophie from her perch on the back of the sofa. 'Wait a minute, horror! No, Jenny, it's just a Victorian-style setting.'

'But the stones,' I said. 'I know it's awful of me to be so ignorant, but what are they? They're not opals and they're not pearls . . .'

'They're moonstones. I must say, I'd never seen them before either. Moth spent a fortnight trying to locate some. I was beginning to think he was stalling!' She examined the ring lovingly, angling her spread fingers to bounce the fiery light from the milk-white gems.

Suddenly, she broke out of her private dream and stood up. 'Anyway, Jenny, I didn't ask you over to show you my ring. Well, yes, I did. But there's something else I wanted to show you as well.'

She reached over the back of the sofa and pulled up the object that had been far more interesting to the two-year-old than her mother's new engagement ring. It was a very large drawing pad.

'Sophie and I have been painting!'

'Really? Can I see?'

'Mine a boat,' announced Sophie, and a very creditable boat it was, too. Nice to know mother's talents were being passed on.

'I had a bump, and Lisa had a bump, and . . .'

'She means bunks,' said Helen. 'But look, what do you think of these?'

With Sophie's efforts carefully spread on the floor by the kitchen door, where the artist bent to talk to them, Helen now pulled out three further sheets from the giant pad and laid them on the carpet at my feet.

'There. What do you think?'

'They're beautiful,' I said. 'What are they?'

Helen laughed. 'We've already had this conversation once! They're placards. Or at least, they will be when Moth sticks them on to hardboard, and nails them to their bits of wood.'

I could hardly believe the words were hand-painted. They looked like printed posters; bold but informal letters all set with shadows behind them.

'Wait a minute,' I said, as I sorted out the legend into a more familiar order. 'You've got JOY on that one, LOVE there, and . . . I get it. Galatians, isn't it? Love, Joy, Peace, Patience, and all those? The fruits of the Spirit?'

'That's it.' Helen arranged the sheets to read LOVE, JOY, PEACE.

'Patience is done in pencil waiting to be painted, and then after that there's all the long words. They're more of a problem. You know, Kindness, Goodness, Faithfulness, Humility and Self-control.'

She saw the thinly-disguised bewilderment behind my polite nod and answered my unspoken question.

'They're for Sunday, Jenny. For Walking Day. It was Moth's idea.'

'Oh. I see. You mean instead of the old embroidered banners?'

'Great heavens, no!' she laughed. 'Not unless you fancy being hung, drawn and quartered. Aunty Knowles helped to do the stitching on the 'Suffer Little Children' banner, you know.'

I didn't know, but I wasn't surprised. The Girls' Bible Class did them at about the time of the Great War.

'Moth just thought Walking Day could be up-dated a bit. We're going to ask Charles if the Playgroup Mums and Toddlers can carry these as their contribution.'

'I think that's a splendid idea!' I said.

And so did Charles.

'Great stuff!' he said, slamming a filing cabinet drawer noisily to emphasize his enthusiasm. 'About time we brought Walking Day into the twentieth century. You can get hidebound by the old traditions, Jenny.'

'That's not what you said when the government pinched our Whit Monday off us all those years ago.'

He pretended to be puzzled. 'Oh. What did I say?'

'Something like, "why can't the morons keep their hands off our heritage"! You were all set to turn our Whit Walk into a full-scale demo.'

'Ah, yes. I do remember. But that was before I realized what a favour they were doing to us, pushing everything into just two days. I mean, it *was* a bit of an ordeal. Parish concert on the Saturday, special services and Short Walk on the Sunday, Long Walk and field games on the Monday. No, I like it better this way. Now, let's have a coffee and you can check me on my lines for the dress rehearsal.'

Neither Moth nor Charles was particularly delighted at the idea of putting curlers in their hair, paint on their faces and balloons up their jumpers for their sketch in the parish concert. In fact, Moth was losing sleep over it. But laughing at the clergy in drag is another parish tradition, cherished every bit as much as any embroidered banner.

I'm not sure how many of my clergy-wife predecessors

have actually been featured in the annual ladies' chorus complete with top-hat, tails, tap-shoes and a fair display of middle-aged spread, but I joined in anyway.

It never goes right on the night, of course. That's another tradition. My two men brought the house down just by stepping on to the stage, Charles as a well-endowed matron and Moth as a flimsily-dressed curvaceous model.

I watched from the wings as they went into their carefully-rehearsed dialogue, ending with Charles saying, 'Dressed like that, you could catch pneumonia!'

To which Moth should have answered, 'Dressed like this, I can catch anything I choose!' Only, he was so nervous, bless him, he said, 'Dressed like this, I can choose anything I catch.'

There was quite a bit of laughter, even so, but when Charles bailed him out with, 'Don't you mean, dressed like that you can catch anything you choose?' and Moth put his hand to his mouth and coloured up in mortification, the audience thought it was just riotous.

There weren't too many smiles, however, when we met to get into procession order at two o'clock the following afternoon.

'I call it a real cheek!'

'It's not as if they're pretty like the old ones, either.'

'They're not even fabric! Just paper and wood!'

'And all that modern writing!'

'As if Canon Coldshaw's lovely banners aren't good enough!'

Such was the rumbling in the ranks of the Ladies' Guild when I joined them behind their banner.

Walking order from time immemorial has always been clergy and choir (if any) leading the procession, ahead of the Sunday School with their 'Suffer Little Children To Come Unto Me' banner, then the Ladies' Guild with

'Martha and Mary', and finally the Men's Bible Class with 'They Left Their Nets And Followed Him'.

But this year, Charles had asked Rita if the Playgroup Mums and Toddlers would like a proper place in the procession now that they were a bona fide and thriving church organization. He'd thought they'd go well between the Sunday School and the Ladies' Guild. They'd liked the idea, and were thrilled with Helen's placards, which nine of them now carried aloft while the others took charge of the buggies and pushchairs. Helen carried 'LOVE.' Most appropriate, I thought!

Any misgivings about Aunty Knowles's reaction to the rival banners were dispelled when I saw her approach Helen before we set off. 'Now don't forget, dear. If little Sophie gets clingy, I'll carry your placard for you.'

Personally, I think Canon Coldshaw would have been delighted with the young mums and I'd have preferred to be up in front with them and their bright new placards. But I sensed that the uneasy tension would have erupted into a full-scale mutiny if I'd forsaken my 'Vicar's Wife' position at the head of the Ladies' Guild. Still, at least the sun was shining as we set off along Balfour Road singing our usual 'opener', 'Let us with a gladsome mind'. And the non-Anglican or non-churchgoing parishioners who lined the street to wave us on our way were suitably touched by the sight of the Sunday School children, decked out this year in white and green, looking like clusters of lily-of-the-valley.

Three or four hymns later, as I watched the front-runners (well, walkers!) turn right at the Post Office crossroads, I caught the children's green prints against the handful of red choir robes beyond and it struck me that the photographs in the local rag would be quite spectacular now that they'd gone over to web offset and colour printing.

As if to give me another glimpse of the pleasing colour contrast, two choir-robes suddenly went into reverse and blended in with the children's smocks and shirts.

'Goodness, what's happening?' I said, to no one in particular.

Edna Jones, immediately behind me, caught me up and said, 'Look, Mrs B. We've stopped!'

Something up Perth Street, our right turn, was obviously blocking our way, despite the fact that we'd always arranged the route and everything with the police ages in advance.

When, above the questioning mutters of all the concertina-ed marchers, I heard shouting from Perth Street, I said to Edna, 'I think I'd better nip up and see what's happening.'

And that's how I found Charles and Moth and our two choir men remonstrating with the leaders of another procession which had obviously been heading *down* Perth Street as ours had attempted to march *up*! But this was not another Whit Walk. For a moment I wasn't sure who they were, I was so taken aback by their haphazard appearance after our neat choir-robes and lily-of-the-valley children. They were mostly a rather bohemian lot with plenty of denim, but a good deal of dressiness too. Women's Rights? Peace Campaigners? My mind went into 'picture-search' as I tried to recall recent issues in the local press. But my eyes were brought to 'freeze-frame' by their placards.

'Gays smash Victorian hypocrisy!'

'Gays can walk too!'

I bit my lip nervously.

Charles was talking to a young person of boyish build with heavily made-up eyelids. 'I know you have rights, Robin. All I'm saying is you should have got police permission for your march.'

'We did ask,' said the young man, 'but we were refused because of your Whit Walk.'

'Naturally,' said Charles. 'We always walk on Pentecost Sunday. Why on earth didn't you choose a different day?'

'The police suggested next week when it's the holiday weekend, but we're all going to a rally in Trafalgar Square. Anyway, why should the Church get preferential treatment on the calendar?'

Robin's band of followers, close enough to hear his speech, cheered their leader, and as their shouts faded I was aware of Josh, robed up as an occasional chorister, at my elbow.

Suddenly he shouted, 'Hey, look! His eyeshadow's the same colour as yours, Dad!'

The jubilant howls, whistles and jeers that erupted after this revelation completely drowned Charles's apoplectic protestations and Moth's uncharacteristic bellow, 'That was *different*, you young idiot!'

Just when I thought Mr Greenwood was about to resort to fisticuffs in defence of his vicar, a strident voice penetrated the melée. 'Gangway! Gangway! Great mercy, if it doesn't take a woman to sort out a muddle.'

It was Aunty Knowles. She was carrying Helen's LOVE banner and as she said the word 'woman' she took a momentary second glance at the green eyeshadow. But she didn't flinch.

'Right,' she said, addressing the Gay-March leader. 'Where are you heading from here?'

I suppose Robin was caught on a reflex because he answered without demur, 'Right from here, up High Bank Street.'

'Well, *that's* no problem, is it? If we keep *our* marchers to their right as they turn up *here*, and you keep *your* marchers to their right as they turn up *there*, we'll just pass each other on the junction.' And without waiting for further consultation, she turned to the church procession and shouted, 'Everyone keep to the right. All right?' Then she did a smart about-turn and gave the opposition marchers the same instruction, before walking back to the centre of the crossroads to call, 'Come on, then. Come on! Everybody, get going. *March*!'

The two processions slowly got moving again, and I ran down the pavement to take up my position in front of Edna. We all kept to the right of the road, as instructed, and as we turned at the crossroads there she was, bless her, slap in the middle, using Helen's LOVE banner as a sort of traffic-policeman's arm, keeping the groups away from each other as they momentarily overlapped.

On impulse I broke ranks and ran to whisper in her ear. 'Aunty Knowles, you're marvellous. Canon Coldshaw would be proud of you.'

There *were* pictures of the children and the choir in Friday's paper. But the biggest picture of all was of Aunty Knowles, waving her placard, under the caption, 'Love still makes the world go round.'

10 June

❊ Summer Fair? Some are Foul!

I do envy the French. Every tiny village plans its annual fête without a thought to the weather. They book military bands, marching girls, travelling fun-fairs and mobile open-air discos with deliciously untainted anticipation. They plan cycle races, children's games and fireworks on the football field knowing that people will only begin to drift away some time after midnight. Nowhere in France would you see a fête poster with the words, (in French, of course), 'Inside if Wet'.

In our part of the world it would make more sense to plan a programme of indoor events and spice the anticipation with the promise 'Outside if Fine'! Not that we haven't had our share of sunny summer fairs, but people do tend to remember the time the gale blew all the stalls down or the year we had snow in June. (It was only a freak flurry that blew over from the moors a full three weeks before our do, but it was a bit too close for comfort for some people.) So when the last Saturday of June dawned warm and clear, in the promise of continuing the heatwave that had been cooking slowly since Wednesday, there were sighs of relief and even shouts of joy all over our parish.

'Another scorcher. Praise the Lord!' said Charles as he swished back the bedroom curtains.

Over breakfast, Drew said, 'There! I told you we wouldn't need to do any hot-dogs. I reckon I'll make a fortune just on the orange juice.'

'Hey, Mum, where's the watering-can?' asked Josh after we'd cleared away. 'I've got a great idea.'

'I think it's in the garage, in the wheelbarrow,' I said. 'Why? What are you planning?'

'Well, all the kids have been changing into their swimming things after school, haven't they? I suppose they'll all be in their trunks and stuff today as well, to keep cool. So I'm going to run the garden hose from the outside tap up to the garden roof, then use the watering-can to shower people when they're hot. Twenty pence a canful. Good, hey?'

'You mean you'll be on the roof, filling up the watering-can and emptying it over your friends?' Trust Josh to come up with something just a little more original than roll-a-penny and hoop-la.

'Yes! I'll take a couple of buckets up with me to run the hose into while I'm watering.'

'Ask Dad, won't you?' I called after him as he went in search of the necessary equipment.

Oh, it *was* nice to be sure of the weather for once. Especially this year, when the committee had decided that all the stalls run by the various church groups should be decorated with specific summer flowers. Suddenly it seemed worth all the bent wire, shredded paper and frayed temper that had gone into the Ladies Guild paper-flower evenings. From the kitchen window I could see our cake stall, a mass of very creditable cornflowers, quite life-like in the morning sun. Rita's poppies were magnificent too. She's so good at that sort of thing, and of course she'd had Helen helping her Playgroup Mums with the toy stall. The Men's Bible Class buttercups were apparently the super-economy size, but were quite effective if you didn't ask what they were.

All round the garden stood the decorated stalls, looking

like a flower show. And soon they'd be manned by their matching decorated helpers. Oh yes, the committee insisted, we'd all have to dress as flowers, to maximize the effect.

I wasn't so keen on that bit, to be honest. Perhaps if I didn't have two teenage sons and a husband with a wicked sense of humour I shouldn't have minded so much. But when I emerged after lunch wearing my home-made costume, a blue crêpe-paper confection with a drooping tutu of a skirt, a precariously tight bodice, and a hat like a bright blue chimney brush, they were predictably hysterical.

'Don't tell me,' Charles said, with mock sobriety. 'I remember it well. It was your going-away outfit, wasn't it?'

Before I could think of a crushing reply Drew said, 'Quick, Josh! Where's your watering-can? There's one here that's wilting!'

Josh, in fact, was quite impressed, in his own way. 'Gosh, Mum. Did you make it all yourself? It's great. What are you meant to be?'

'I'm a cornflower, stupid! And if you think *this* is funny, wait till you see Aunty Knowles. She's in the Olde English Tea Shoppe . . .'

'You mean the church hall,' corrected Drew.

'. . . And *they're* all dressed as old English flowers.'

'Well?' asked Charles. 'So what's *she* dressing up as?'

'A shrinking violet!' And on that note of triumph I went out into the garden to take my place at the cake stall with Edna and the others, in good time before the gates opened and the hordes swarmed in.

But just before horde-swarming time, Charles came dashing over looking very agitated. 'Hey, Jen, I'm worried. It's two minutes to go, and she's not here yet.'

'Who?' I asked, wondering if we should slice up a huge

bunloaf and make more profit on single pieces.

'Our guest opener. The Lovely Lucinda Lestrick,' said Charles, quoting our posters. 'Radio Moorland's Delectable Lady Disc Jockey.'

'Oh. You mean Lucy Lastic,' I said, using her universal nickname. 'Oh, she'll be here in a tick. She only lives across the park.'

'No, that's just it, Jenny. She's coming up from London. Been doing a recording or something. She should have been on the one o'clock train.'

'Well, if she was she'd have been here by now.'

'That's what I mean.' Charles looked at his watch anxiously, then at me. 'Look, Jen, if I let them in and give them a bit of flannel with the welcome, will you nip down to the station and see what's happened?'

There are times when a clergy marriage is stretched almost to breaking point. This was one of them. 'Like *this?*' I shrieked. 'Oh Charles, don't be ridiculous. It's bad enough standing behind a stall in my own garden, but drive down to the station? You've got to be joking!'

I thought I'd snapped, like a taut rubber band. But perhaps I'd only sagged, like a thread of well-chewed gum. Because three minutes later I was in our car heading for the station, and any hopes I might have entertained of keeping a low profile in my guise as a cornflower were dashed by the fact that Helen had insisted on coming with me, for company, and she'd brought Sophie along too. One unaccompanied cornflower might just have escaped notice. A cornflower in the company of two poppies didn't stand a chance. The Saturday shoppers on the pedestrian crossing outside the bus-station couldn't believe their eyes. They stopped walking, nudged each other and pointed at the oddballs in the car with the crazy headgear, until I revved and hooted them out of our path.

'It'll be even worse at the station,' I moaned.

That was wicked of me. I only said it in the hope that Helen would offer to jump out and make enquiries whilst I kept the engine running.

Helen said nothing.

'Serves you right!' I told myself, but as I glanced across at her I realized that she wasn't keeping silent out of stubbornness. She was totally — and morosely, it seemed to me — preoccupied.

Sophie, who from the back of the car had been poking her poppy-hatted head between ours so as not to miss anything, suddenly got bored, and I watched her frilly bottom obliterate my rearview mirror as she climbed up to look out of the back window.

The relative privacy allowed me to ask quietly, 'What's the matter, Helen? Not feeling too good?'

'No, I'm fine, Jenny. Really.'

She studied her fingers as they plucked at her red paper skirt. 'It's just . . . well . . . Moth and I . . .'

We were turning into Midland Square and I caught her face as I looked for a gap between the passing taxis. She was crying. I swung into an empty fifteen-minute parking place.

'Had a row? Is that it? It's quite usual in the run-up to a wedding, you know. Don't let it get you down.'

Helen brushed the tears from under her eyes with the ends of her fingers in a careful, artistic gesture, and swallowed.

'No. We haven't rowed. It's just that I don't think I can marry him, Jenny. It wouldn't be right.'

The pit of my stomach churned with sympathy, impatience and, most of all, anger.

'Not right? Now listen, Helen. If anyone's said anything about you having Sophie . . .'

She looked at me steadily, her serious brown eyes willing me to understand.

'Jenny, it's not that. We've talked it through, and it's not a problem to either of us. Moth loves Sophie like she was his own. You know that.'

It was true. They made a lovely family even in these days before the actual wedding.

A tiny part of my mind pressed me to remember why I was sitting outside the station. But I had to get to the bottom of Helen's strange behaviour.

'Well then?'

She was looking down at her hands again. 'I'm not like you, Jenny. I could never be a clergyman's wife. I'd be a millstone.'

'You *what*? I never heard anything so silly. Why, you're an asset to Moth already. You'd be an asset to any church. You've so much talent.'

'I'd be an asset to any club that needed a poster painter or a children's helper or a tea lady.'

She looked up at me again with some urgency.

'Don't you see, Jenny? Anyone's wife could do that sort of stuff. But a clergyman's wife has to be, well, a proper Christian.'

So that was it.

'And you think you're not?'

'I'm not sure.'

'Have you told Moth how you feel?'

'No. It sounds so ridiculous. But it matters to me, Jenny. Really it does. I'd feel a fraud marrying Moth.'

I could see the problem was insurmountable in her eyes, so I resisted the temptation to dismiss her feelings as silly. I opened the car door, but before I got out I turned to her.

'Helen, I think I know what you're saying. But I also think you're being very unfair to Moth, not telling him the reason for your sudden reluctance. Think about it.'

With this new worry on my mind, the stares of porters and passengers mattered little to me now. I discovered that the London train had arrived on time without mishap, that no messages had been left, and that there was no one remotely like Lucinda Lestrick coasting about the place looking lost.

Helen and I drove back to the vicarage in silence, with Sophie making up for this by chattering nineteen to the dozen and waving at puzzled pedestrians. We found the Summer Fair in full swing on our return.

'You've been ages!' Charles accused. 'Can't think why. Lucy Lastic phoned just after you left to say she'd missed the train.'

I was too deflated to be irritated.

'Who opened it, then? You?'

'No. Didn't need to. Mr Greenwood found this military bloke in the queue. Retired something-or-other. Nobody knew him from Adam, but he stepped in and did the honours anyway. Gave us a marvellous send-off and threatened to put them all on jankers if they didn't spend a fortune.'

I managed a smile.

'Oh, Mrs B., there you are. Did we say we'd slice this bunloaf?'

'Here's Edna. I'd better get to my stall. Charles, will you meet me for tea in the hall later?'

I'd have to tell him about Helen and Moth.

'Fine. Say about four o'clock?'

He kissed my nose and went to throw darts at coloured cards.

By the time I found a table for two in the Olde English Tea Shoppe set out in the church hall I was more than ready for two cups, or even three, from Aunty Knowles' teapot. My paper costume was sticking to me in the heat, and as my fingers were dyed blue from the scores of times I'd pushed my hat off my forehead, I knew I must be blue all over under the outfit. I was idly wondering how long it would take for the dye to wear off and how many parishioners would be poisoned by cakes served them from my inky fingers, when Charles joined me.

'Gosh, Jenny, it's going really well. Reckon we'll have taken hundreds. Praise the Lord for the sunshine, eh?' He smiled at me over his teacup.

'Charles, Helen and I had a talk when we went to the station.'

'So that's why you took so long! I should have known better than to send two women.'

'Hush, silly, and listen.'

But before I could tell him of Helen's dilemma, Mr Greenwood came weaving towards us, bumping into chairs and tables in his haste and causing a fair bit of tea-spilling and tongue-clicking.

'Vicar! Vicar! He's gone. Vamoosed! Done a bunk with all the takings!'

'What? What are you talking about? Who do you mean? Come on, now, Bernard. Take a deep breath and talk sense.'

'That colonel fellow! Being ever so helpful, he was. Saw how busy we were with the crowds and that. Offered to go and collect all the takings so far from the stall-holders, in case of petty theft. You know, said we shouldn't leave them with too much money on the stalls with the risk and everything. So I'm there waiting for him in the vestry, ready to start counting the money when he brings it, only he *doesn't* bring it! He's gone!'

'What? Good grief! Jenny, phone the police. I'll search the garden and the street, in case he's still in the vicinity.

Oh, why didn't it rain? This wouldn't have happened if we'd all been inside.'

The policeman on the other end of the phone was being very patient with me as I tried to give him details of a man I'd never seen. 'Just a simple description, ma'am. Age, height, colouring. That sort of thing.' Fortunately, Charles came into the study at that point and I handed over to him.

Back in the garden, the last of the customers were picking their way through the crisp packets and trampled paper flowers, offering commiserations.

'Terrible shame, having a thief among us.'

'Disgusting, isn't it? Stealing from the Church.'

'Him and his fancy moustache. I know what *I'd* do if I got hold of it!'

I started pulling the cornflowers off our empty cake stall, and throwing them into a rubbish bag. Helen was similarly occupied with the playgroup's poppies. Sophie was trying to help, tearing off pieces where she could, and throwing them over her shoulder with infant abandon.

'Oh, stop that, Sophie!' Helen scolded. 'I've had just about enough for one day.'

'Me too,' I said to myself. 'If I don't have a bath soon I'll get St Vitus' dance.'

Into this gloomy pall came a sudden and incongruous shout. 'Hi there, everybody! Look who made it at last! Better late than never!'

And striding into the garden from the church hall gate came the lovely Lucinda Lestrick — all spiked blonde hair, black eyes, and red and purple checked trouser suit. Lucy Lastic! What on earth good did she think she could do turning up after they'd all just about gone home? I think I might have vented my spleen on the poor woman if Charles hadn't spotted her from the vicarage and come out to greet her.

'Hi, Rev!' sang Lucy. 'Sorry I goofed up your fête. I couldn't just cut home without a word. I gather you had a ball without me anyway.'

'Well, er, yes and no,' said Charles, obviously wondering whether to compound the girl's guilt by telling her about her light-fingered understudy.

'I'd have been even later if it hadn't been for these two gorgeous policemen.'

I'd half wondered how such a minor radio star came to have such an impressive bodyguard.

'They brought me here straight from the train. Bit of a fracas with a gentleman getting into my compartment as I was getting out. All about St Cuthbert's, so I cadged a lift. Is the Olde English Tea Shoppe still open? I could murder a cup of tea!'

And she tripped over to the hall, to cause innocent mayhem with Aunty Knowles' sensibilities.

The policemen didn't actually have our money in a bag labelled 'loot'. But they and their colleagues *had* picked up the colonel at the station after our phone call. Apparently, he was a well-known con-man and easily spotted.

'If you'd care to call in at your earliest convenience, Vicar,' said one of the officers to Charles, 'we'll do all the necessary to make sure all the money comes back to you.'

'I say,' said Charles, 'I'm not sure it would be all ours. We hadn't counted it.'

'Don't you worry, sir. It was still in the padded envelopes with the names of the stalls on them. I'll give you a ring later and tell you how much, just so you'll know.'

Charles took the policemen into the church hall for a celebratory cup of tea, and I decided to go and get my bath. Between the garage and the kitchen the heavens opened. The sudden downpour from such a clear sky took me so completely by surprise that I stood still, just long enough to get soaked to the skin through the disintegrating crêpe-paper. Then the deluge stopped as suddenly as it had started and I looked up. And saw the watering-can.

'Sorry, Mum. Couldn't resist it! You looked as if you needed freshening up.'

I was beyond words. So I lifted the soggy giant cornflower off my dripping hair and threw it at him. Bullseye!

I didn't bother waiting for a prize.

11 July

❊ Beside the Seaside

I looked at my watch. Nearly ten past eight. If Helen didn't come soon, we'd have to assume she'd decided to keep a low profile. Charles had checked the list for the front bus, the one I was on. Just Helen and Sophie missing. The other double-decker behind us was full and ready to go. Moth had the list for that one.

From my front upstairs seat I heard Charles clattering up the steel steps. He'd come to confer. 'What do you think, Jen? Want to go round and see if she's coming, or what?'

But a cheer from below told us Helen was here, and Charles retreated.

As the bus shuddered with the starting of the engine, Sophie's head bobbed up the stair-well, and I got up to give her a hand. Once she was safely settled on my knee, I turned to her mother who'd slipped in alongside me.

'I thought you might have changed your mind. About the trip, I mean.'

'I did. A million times. But I don't want to leave the church just because I can't bring myself to marry the curate. Besides, Sophie needs new shoes.' She was trying to keep her voice light and confident, but I sensed her deep unhappiness and my heart ached for her.

'Red ones.' Sophie's excitement at the prospect of new footwear meant this wasn't the time for a serious conversation. So I prayed that Helen would open up a little and talk, perhaps later on. People do, on church outings.

She smiled at me, almost as if she could read my thoughts. 'Where are we going, anyway? It's all a bit muddly in my mind still.'

'Of course,' I said. 'I forgot you didn't come last year. This is a repeat run by popular demand. It's the shoes first. Bobby Hall's Warehouse, the one on the TV adverts. Incredible place, really it is. I mean, there's all these thousands of cut-price shoes in this huge converted textile mill. Three full floors. Or is it four? Anyway, it's enormous. And apart from the shoes, there's a restaurant with toilets, so it's ideal for a coffee break before we go on to the coast.'

'And that's the sit-down lunch, then, isn't it? The sandwiches are for tea-time?'

'That's right. Again, by popular demand. The Little Brown Jug at Moorside Bay. Very traddy — plaice, chips and peas, apple pie and custard, choice of tea or coffee. But really excellent and very reasonable.'

And we nattered on, both of us deliberately avoiding the heavy stuff, with Sophie chipping in as she played with the contents of her bright red plastic holdall.

There were already several coaches in the show warehouse car park, but ours were the first double-deckers. Doubtless there'd be more during the day. The place is as popular as Madam Tussaud's.

As our party drifted into the carpeted foyer, the canned pop music faded and a slick disc jockey presenter enthused at us from the speakers. 'Hello to all from Bobby Hall's, the good news when you're buying shoes. And a special welcome to our friends just arriving with the St Cuthbert's parish outing!'

There were hoots of delight and amazement at this, and

shouts of, 'Come on in, quick! We're on the wireless!' But no, the regulars amongst us knew that the all-day music show came from the dais at the centre of the top fashion department on the ground floor.

'Take your time, ladies and gents,' the mid-atlantic voice crooned at us, 'and you will find the bargain of a lifetime. That's a Bobby Hall guarantee. And now, just for you, St Cuthbert's, here's this week's number six and climbing fast . . .'

'The children's shoes are down here,' I said to Helen, 'but I think I'll have to go up to the men's department with Drew. He's into eights already.'

It was with some difficulty that I equipped Josh and Drew with new school shoes for the autumn. Apart from the obvious problem of guessing how much their feet would be likely to grow during the summer, there was the unavoidable distraction of acres of totally unsuitable items, enticing my two like flowers tempting bees.

'Hey, Mum, look at these. They've got zips and pockets! Aren't they great?' Josh had climbed into a pair of enormous shocking-pink padded moonboots that looked as if they might double as a couple of weekend bags.

'But not for school, Josh.'

Meanwhile, Drew sauntered towards us in a pair of white leather ankle boots with pointed toes and elastic sides. 'You know, these are remarkably comfy. Smart, too.'

'Yes. But not for school!'

Charles had his own problems, sifting through hundreds of casual sports shoes trying to find himself something sensible and waterproof rather than fashionable and flimsy.

Eventually, after buying myself some canvas slip-ons, I caught up with Helen in the restaurant. Charles and Moth had collected their coffee and joined a group of older ladies of the parish who were rejoicing at their bargain bedroom slippers and broad-fitting gold dance shoes. Drew and Josh took Sophie to watch the disc jockey and his flashing lights, and I thankfully dumped my bags in one chair and collapsed into another, opposite Helen.

'Gosh, I'm glad that's over!'

As we drank our coffee, I admired the red leather sandals she'd found for Sophie, and I told her about the Battle of the Moonboots.

She smiled. 'Do you find it difficult, combining the role of vicar's wife with ordinary mother?'

'No!' I laughed. Then I admitted, 'Well, yes, I suppose I do sometimes. But it's the only life I know, and I wouldn't swap it.'

Helen looked thoughtful, and I prayed that if she was summoning up the courage to talk about her and Moth, the Lord would give me the right things to say.

'You'd find it much harder, though, wouldn't you, if you didn't share Charles's faith?'

'Yes, I expect I would. I suppose if I didn't have the same spiritual outlook as Charles, I wouldn't be able to catch his vision for the parish and help him in it. I'd try, of course, because I love him. But I imagine it would be a bit like being blind, or working in the dark.'

'And I expect it would upset Charles to see you so helpless. And then you'd be upset because you'd upset him.'

'It sounds a bit complicated!' I said. 'Anyway, it's all very hypothetical.'

Helen looked at me with a directness that held both a challenge and an SOS. 'But that's *it*, you see, Jen. It's not hypothetical for me and Moth. That's what it would be like if I married him. I'd hold him back. It wouldn't be fair.

We'd both be miserable.'

I decided to ignore the challenge and acknowledge the distress signal, and I clutched at the air prayerfully for the words. 'Yes, you would. And no one would want to force the two of you into a lifetime of misery together.'

While Helen poked at the demerara sugar, saying nothing, I threw her what I hoped was a lifeline. 'So it's a good job there's an alternative, isn't it?'

The dark lashes lifted at once. 'How do you mean?'

'Just that the hypothetical situation is only one side of the coin. It describes the problem, but doesn't present a solution.'

'Is there one?'

'I think so, if I'm hearing you right.'

'Go on,' she said, 'I want to know what it is.'

'Well, correct me if I'm wrong, but here's how it looks to me when you boil it down. You and Moth are incompatible because your faith is somehow not in line with his, right?'

'Right.'

'Two observations come to mind. Number one: incompatibility is not a life-sentence. It only needs one or both parties to be flexible.'

'Oh, but I wouldn't want Moth to compromise his beliefs.'

'Fair enough. Then the onus is on you when it comes to making adjustments. Anyway, that was only number one. Number two: the reason for the incompatibility is that you're not sure you're a proper Christian in the way that Moth is. Right?'

'Right again.'

'Well, again, fair enough. So it's down to you to check the facts and find out exactly what it means to be a

Christian. It's not an exclusively clergy prerogative, you know.'

'I know. I've been talking to Rita. She's a lovely Christian, isn't she?'

I nodded. 'And what does Rita say?'

'She quotes the Bible!' Helen shrugged and smiled.

'Well, it's not all prophets and Philistines,' I said. 'You could do a lot worse than search the Scriptures if you want to know what a real Christian is.'

We noticed other members of our party gathering up their parcels and making their way out to the car park.

'Time to break camp,' Helen said. 'Can we talk on the bus?'

But we were passed so many shoes to admire, and Sophie had to be escorted while she showed off her new sandals, so we were rolling along the promenade at Moorside Bay before we'd had a chance to pick up the threads of our conversation.

Lunch was a bit noisy, because although we were all seated in sixes right through The Little Brown Jug's three dining rooms, everyone wanted to talk to everyone, or so it seemed. And now and then some funny remark would cause a wave of laughter that rippled from room to room. Helen and Sophie sat with Rita and her husband and two little girls. She seemed quite relaxed, and I was pleased.

After lunch, people went off to do their own thing, find their own tea or picnic, promising to be back at the pier kiosk at six o'clock.

'The boys want to go to the funfair,' said Charles. 'Do you want to come, Jen? Or have you made other plans?'

I hadn't, but I certainly didn't relish the Big Dipper after fish and chips.

I was saved by Aunty Knowles. 'I'm taking Moth and

Sophie to the Tiny Tots' Fun Centre,' she announced, letting us know she'd done some advance research, 'and back here for a cream tea. Only Helen says she'd rather see the shops. Are you going round the shops or what?'

So Helen and I set off together after arranging to meet Charles and the boys on the beach later for a picnic.

The sun was warm on our backs as we wandered slowly down the main street, pausing to laugh at the postcards, or admire the glassware, or marvel at the expensive dresses. At the memorial park, we bought ice-creams and found an empty bench in the rose garden. It was lovely to sit there surrounded by the fragrance of the flowers, all my troubles reduced to licking the ice-cream from the cone before it ran melting into my fingers in the heat of the sun.

Presently, Helen said, 'Could you explain the Bible to me, Jenny?'

'Not all of it,' I protested. 'And certainly not in the space of an afternoon.'

'Silly! I mean, if I remember bits I've heard from Rita, would you tell me what they mean?'

'If I can, of course. But wouldn't you rather ask Moth? Or Charles?'

'I don't think so. I think I need to know I'm talking to a Christian who's not a clergyman. Do you understand?'

'Perfectly,' I said. 'Fire away!'

'Well, it's odd words, really. Like sin. And repent. I mean, I know my copybook's blotted forever because of Sophie, but I've been trying to be good. Only Rita quotes things about everyone being a sinner, not just people like me.'

'"All have sinned", you mean? It's true. No one's perfect, and that's the only standard acceptable to God.'

'Then we're all in the same boat?'

'Exactly. Which is why the Bible tells us to repent. That

means turn round. Deliberately renounce the tendency within us that pulls us away from perfection. And apologize, say we're sorry to God.'

'But perfection's not that easy, surely? And anyway, where does Jesus come in?'

'You've got it in one!' I said. 'Because God is a God of love, he wants us to be part of his family forever. But because God is also a God of justice, he can't turn a blind eye to our sin. So he provided someone, someone special, someone innocent without any debts on his own account, to serve our sentence, pay the price, take the punishment on our behalf.'

'Jesus. Yes, I see,' said Helen. 'That fits. "God so loved the world . . ." how does it go?'

'"That he gave his only son Jesus, so that whoever believes in him should not perish but have eternal life."'

'But we're still not perfect?'

'Well, we're still mortal, and we still hurt God by sinning. But believing in Jesus means believing that our punishment has been taken, by Jesus, and the sin wiped off the slate, so to speak, when we repent and ask his forgiveness.'

'A clean slate?' Helen pursed her lips thoughtfully. 'I didn't know about that.' After a pause, she said, 'And what is eternal life, exactly?'

'Living as part of God's family forever. Here and now in this imperfect world, *and* after we die in God's perfect Heaven.'

'I like that,' Helen said. 'The family bit.'

The ice-creams were well finished and forgotten. We sat in silence for several minutes. Helen had her eyes closed. She could have been sunbathing. Suddenly she said, 'So what does "born again" mean? I know it's something of a jargon phrase these days in the papers, but it's in the Bible, isn't it?'

'It is,' I said. 'In fact, Charles says most of what you read in the papers is in the Bible in one form or another! Being born again means starting a whole new life, motivated by a new life-force. Not in the physical sense, obviously, but in the spiritual dimension. That point in life when a person makes a conscious and adult decision to acknowledge their general sinfulness, to accept God's remedy by turning to Jesus, to ask him to forgive them and live within them by his Spirit — really, it's just like a new birth. Hence the phrase.'

'When you say "by his Spirit", is that the Holy Spirit?'

'Yes. If it weren't for the power and the patience of God's Spirit within us, it'd be back to the old routine of trying to reach perfection by tugging at our own bootstraps. Fast road to despair, I'd say.'

'You mean being good is easier with the Holy Spirit in you?'

'I suppose I do, but it sounds a bit holier-than-thou put like that. He's called "the Helper" in the Bible. He helps us, if we let him.'

'I see. And anyway, once the perfection problem's been sorted out by believing in Jesus, you'd be relieved of the pressure of trying to make yourself good *just* to get into *Heaven*, wouldn't you?'

'Now you're teaching me,' I joked.

Helen sighed thoughtfully and looked up at a wispy white cloud blowing in from the sea.

'Can I just do a quick fingertip recap.? All have sinned; no one's perfect; Jesus took the punishment; a person who believes *that* actually *is* perfect in God's eyes; born-again is when a person admits all this seriously and turns to Jesus for forgiveness; the Holy Spirit comes to live in the born-again person to help them; and they are then part of God's family forever. Is that the main gist of it all?'

'Wow!' I laughed and poked her in the ribs. 'You should write that down! It would make a marvellous tract. But you've got it. Come on. Let's see if we can find my lot on the beach.'

I felt quite strongly that if Helen seriously wanted to put herself right with God, and it seemed as if she might, then it ought to be Moth who should pray with her, not me.

Helen was pushing her cardigan into her shopping bag. 'And all this time I'd been thinking it was a case of going to church and being true to your own opinion.' She caught my elbow to stop me strolling off. 'Thanks, Jen. I needed to hear all that.'

Her face lit up suddenly with a mischievous grin. 'Last one to the penny arcade buys the next ice-creams!' And I was left gaping in amazement as she sped like a child along the neat garden paths and disappeared between the majestic gateposts.

It was breezy on the beach, where the parish rounders match was just finishing and the flasks and sandwiches were beginning to appear. Helen stayed long enough to eat one sandwich, then donated the rest of her picnic to Josh and Drew. 'I think I'd better make sure Aunty Knowles is all right with Sophie.'

'Oh, they'll be fine,' said Charles. 'They're with Moth.'

Helen blushed. 'Yes, I know,' she said, and she picked her way through the deck chairs to the concrete steps.

When we gathered together at the pier kiosk ready to board our buses for home, Sophie came to show me her bucket and spade.

'Hello, pickle,' I said. 'Where did you get those?'

'Uncle Moth!' she beamed.

Her mother smiled, and blushed again at the name. 'Moth's asked me to go home on his bus, Jenny.'

'What a lovely idea,' I said. 'Would you like me to have Sophie?'

Helen frowned. 'Oh no,' she said quickly, 'I didn't mean to suggest . . .'

'I know you didn't, but she's bound to sleep, and it's a long time since I had a cuddly infant in my arms.'

'Well, if you're sure, then . . .'

The toddler did sleep, of course. It was Moth who took her from me outside the church hall.

'Let me take Sophie, Jen,' he said. 'I'm seeing Helen home anyway.' He caught the question in my eye as he shifted the load from my arms to his. 'Yes. Everything's fine now,' he said. 'Thanks!'

12 August

❊ Dearly Beloved . . .

'The tent's still up!'

Charles turned from the bedroom window and brought a cup of tea over to the bed where I had just shuffled myself upright.

'It's a marquee,' I reminded him with a yawn. 'And we'd be in queer street if it fell down. I mean, with three hundred guests and no floor in the church hall.' (The parquet blocks had been taken up prior to re-laying, after the playgroup had had a flood.)

I sipped the welcome tea. 'This is nice, tea in bed. Is it the start of a new era?'

'Don't bank on it! I just thought today was special, having a bride married from our house.'

'Mmm. I know what you mean. Having Helen here this week has been like having an instant grown-up daughter. I like it.'

'Don't forget the granddaughter,' said Charles. 'Sophie's been awake since before the birds. She's down in the kitchen now with the boys, prancing about in her nightie and her bridesmaid's hat.'

'Head-dress,' I corrected. 'I do hope she doesn't spoil it!'

But Drew managed to retrieve the little wreath of silk flowers in exchange for a bowl of Weety Crunch, and by the time I was grabbing my own hurried toast, the do-it-yourself buffet-breakfast was nearly finished. Charles was in church, the children were watching TV and Moth had been despatched to the florist's.

As pre-arranged, I took Helen's breakfast up to her room. Just grapefruit, toast and coffee as requested, but laid out on my own grandmother's best traycloth and prettied up with a single rose in a small vase. I was determined to wring every last ounce of enjoyment from my part as Bride's Mother!

'It's a really lovely morning,' I said. 'Did you sleep well?'

'As a matter of fact, Jen, I did. I've been awake for a bit, though. Reading.'

I arranged the tray on her knees. 'Anything special?'

'The Acts of the Apostles in this modern translation Moth gave me. I never knew the Bible could be such an exciting book. That shipwreck on Malta — you know, St Paul — it's so lifelike.'

'Well, I'd hardly call it suitable reading for a wedding day, but I know what you mean!'

Helen tucked into her breakfast with no sign of last-minute butterflies, for which I was thankful.

'You know,' I said, 'it seems a shame to mess about with your hair. It looks beautiful just long and loose like that.'

Helen wrinkled her nose in disapproval. '*You* can't see the knots at the back! And you're certainly not going to talk me out of my trip to André Maurice. I've always admired the way the Royals get their hair pinned up in that lovely bouffant shape. Today's the day I find out how it's done.'

'Oh, I expect you're right,' I said. 'Every girl's a princess on her wedding day.'

Helen cut her toast into dainty pieces.

'You know, Jenny, I'm so lucky. Everything's worked out, well, perfectly. Moth's thesis has been accepted, I've become a real Christian, Sophie's so thrilled to be getting a daddy . . . I'm not dreaming am I?'

'Don't be silly!'

As I spoke, reality asserted itself with a sharp ring at the doorbell. I left the princess to finish eating her breakfast and counting her blessings and ran downstairs.

''Ello, Mrs Belvidere.'

It was Donna, granddaughter of Percy the parrot's owner.

'Me gran sent me round with these for the wedding couple.' She thrust a gift-wrapped flat box at me.

'Well, that *is* kind,' I said, 'and I'm sure Moth and Helen will call and say thank you after their honeymoon.'

Having handed over the parcel, the child now seemed unwilling to walk away from it. 'Er — it's napkins,' she confided. 'Not baby ones. Tablecloth ones. And, erm, *I* wrote the card.'

I was obviously expected to check this out and praise her efforts, so I unfolded the silver wedding bell and read, 'To the happy couple with love from Mrs Burrows, Donna Burrows, and Percy Burrows. XXX.'

It's not every bride who receives a set of table napkins from a parrot!

'Oh, that's lovely, Donna,' I said. 'They'll both be very pleased.'

This was apparently the satisfactory conclusion to the interview that Donna had been hoping for, and she grinned and ran back down the steps.

I put the wrapped box of napkins with all the other wedding presents. Having a marquee for the reception meant that Helen was able to use the dining room to make a beautiful display of the many gifts she and Moth had been given. There were the usual towels and dishes and cheeseboards, but my eye went again to the brown envelope on the sideboard. It was addressed to Helen, and was her proudest possession, shown frequently to visitors. So for the hundredth time I smoothed the single page and read:

'You are hereby given notice to quit the rented apartment in the property known as 78 Wellington Street as from 31 July. Have managed to sell the lot to the man with those video things in the shop downstairs. As I am fairly well suited at Brecondale, please find enclosed his cheque which I have duly endorsed. See me if any difficulty. Yours sincerely, Edith Eliza Knowles. PS Make sure darling Sophie gets her share. PPS Have arranged with vicar for you to go to them 1 August till wedding.'

Of course, Helen hadn't needed a notice to quit before coming to stay with us. But it pleased Aunty Knowles to think she was sorting us all out. What a typical gesture, this letter with the fat cheque pinned to it. She and Helen were proving to be better than family to each other.

At eleven o'clock I took drinks and biscuits in to the TV morons. Normally I'd have bawled them out for wasting the sunshine, but I reasoned that at least this way I shouldn't have to cope with any ill-timed broken limbs, teeth or clothing.

'I'm just popping over to the marquee to help the ladies,' I said.

'You'll love it, Mum,' Josh promised. 'They've put up a frilly pink and white lining since last night.'

'Oh, have you been in this morning, then?'

Drew answered without taking his eyes off the screen. 'Yeah. Got thrown out as usual.'

'Well today of all days we don't want to waste time larking about. Just keep a low profile, would you? I'll be back in good time to bath and dress Sophie and inspect you two. Dad's in church, Moth's gone to collect the flowers, Helen's at the hairdressers, and I'm in the marquee. Wedding's at one, remember.' And I left them to their Tom and Jerry.

Josh was quite right, the inside of the marquee was beautiful. The tent-hire people had been back and completely covered the canvas walls and roof with a pink and white ruched lining. Even the tent poles were gift-wrapped!

Rita McDonald came across as soon as she saw me. 'Great, isn't it, Jenny? Like something out of a Hollywood musical.'

I nodded my enthusiasm. 'It's all so lovely. And just wait till you see the bride.'

'Yes,' said Rita. 'I saw Helen's dress just before she finished it. And Sophie's. They'll look like a couple of princesses.'

'My thoughts exactly. She's at the hairdresser's right now, getting the royal works, facial and everything.'

'Should think so, too,' said Rita. 'Deserves the best, does Helen. Specially today. Come and see the buffet. We've nearly finished.'

Along one side of the marquee's length was a table laden with delicately prepared fingerfoods — vol-au-vents, pies, canapés, rolls, cheeses, fruits, tarts — all lovingly arranged and punctuated with posies of fresh summer flowers.

The Ladies' Guild and the Playgroup Mums had insisted on providing Helen with a wedding reception no orphan ever dreamed of, including the three-tier cake at the centre of the spread, whose model groom, I noticed, even wore a clerical collar!

'You've done wonders, Rita. Is there anything left for me to do?'

'Yes, you can come and help with the punch.'

Near the entrance were two tables where half-a-dozen ladies were chopping fruit and throwing it into six enormous silver containers on the grass nearby.

'They're babybaths!' laughed Rita, without waiting for my question. 'But don't tell anyone; we covered them in kitchen foil.'

'Hello, Mrs B. Would you like to share these buckets between those baths?' Edna indicated three plastic buckets under her table.

As I tipped the inky brown liquid on to the fruit I asked, 'What *is* this, anyway?'

'Very strong cold tea,' said Rita. 'Don't wince. It counteracts the sweetness of the fruit cordial. All we've got to do later is dash over here, six of us, as soon as the service is over, and add six bottles of lemonade to each bath. We have to do that at the last minute because of the fizz.'

'Marvellous,' I said. 'Have you got six ladies, or do you need me?'

'Don't be daft!' Rita scolded, in mock horror. 'You're the Bride's Mother!'

I went to check that the church flowers hadn't done anything silly overnight, and was gratified to find that the white gladioli buds were beginning to open in the warmth, as I'd hoped they would when I chose them for my special Bride's Mother's Church Arrangements.

Charles was writing up the register in the vestry. 'Is the countdown going to plan?' he asked when I looked in on him.

'So far so good,' I said. 'Even the flowers are co-operating.'

'All set for a one o'clock lift-off, then?'

'Barring accidents and acts of God,' I joked.

'This whole thing's an act of God, if you ask me,' he said, and he gave me that knowing look of his, where his inner delight sparkles from the twinkle in his eyes.

Tom and Meg arrived at twelve-thirty, collected one very quiet, very pale groom and two very bouncy but well-scrubbed teenage boys, and Charles took them all over to church. From the kitchen door he called, 'Don't be late!'

'Bride's prerogative!' I yelled back, and I gathered up Justin and Lisa and took them upstairs.

'My, don't you both look a treat?' I said, as they climbed the stairs gingerly, Justin admiring his buckled shoes on every step and Lisa lifting her long cream gown.

Sophie met us on the landing. 'Mine a long dress, too!' she beamed. 'Like my Mummy's.'

Helen had balked at the idea of a white wedding, despite pressure from all sides. 'No,' she'd insisted, 'it wouldn't be right. It would be making a symbolic statement about my status which is patently untrue.' So it was a cream-gowned princess who received us in the guest room.

I'd seen the dress in the making, of course. But I was still stopped in my tracks by the vision at the foot of the bed. The upswept regal hairstyle, the antique gossamer veil (loaned by Aunty Knowles), the extravagantly bouffant taffeta dress with its clever tucks and frills, ('Cheap lining fabric,' Helen had said. 'It'll never wash, but it should be OK on the day'). OK was insultingly insufficient.

I shook my head with maternal disbelief at my good fortune in being allowed this glimpse of fairyland.

'Helen . . .'. The words were hard to find. 'You look stunning. Honestly, our church has never seen such a beautiful bride.'

Helen shrugged with pleasure and excitement, knowing she was looking her prettiest ever. 'It worked, didn't it?' she said. 'And I must say, I've never seen a lovelier Bride's Mother. Do you know, that blue is the exact shade of your eyes?'

The two cream miniatures were arranging themselves either side of Helen's gown to catch some of this free-flowing admiration, whilst the royal page boy admired his own shirt frills in the wardrobe mirror, when the doorbell announced Mr Greenwood's arrival.

'Oops! There's the Bride's Father with the cars.'

I took Sophie's hand, and ushered the other two ahead of me. 'Come on,' I said. 'Time for a drive round the block in a lovely big black limousine.'

I gave Helen a last look. 'See you in church, princess!'

I've never seen St Cuthbert's quite so full, before or since. And because everyone was wearing their absolutely very best Sunday-best, the atmosphere positively crackled with 'special' as Helen came up the aisle on Mr Greenwood's arm to the familiar Wagner tune.

It was that kind of a day. The service went without a hitch. Charles was at his magnetic best, investing every word of the liturgy with warmth and feeling. Neither bride nor groom fluffed a single response, and even the choir, much augmented with friends and relations and even willing strangers, was note-perfect in the psalm. The sun shone, the photographer was charming and efficient, and as the bride's 'family' lined up inside the marquee to welcome the 'open house' guests, the fruit punch fizzed in the silvered punch bowls.

My appreciation of such total perfection prompted me to mutter to Charles out of the side of my mouth between handshakes, 'I didn't know Miss Langford could play the Vidor Toccata?'

'She can't,' came his whispered reply.

'But she did, for the final music. Another miracle?'

'Well, hello! Yes, lovely, isn't it? Do help yourself to the food! No, not another *miracle*. Another *left hand*.'

'I don't get you.'

'Big Beryl. They played half each, one up the top, the other down the bottom. Been practising for weeks. Think they shared the feet, too!'

116

Bless them! Everyone had given themselves one hundred per cent to the success of their curate's marriage to the playgroup helper. And when Irish O'Brien played his handbells before the speeches, by invitation of course, his special version of 'The Bells of St Mary's' was now in harmony, two bells at a time, and not a clanger in sight!

Moth's speech began, 'Ladies and Gentlemen: little did I know when I came to this parish . . .' and was immediately submerged in cheers and applause.

Charles caught my eye with a look that said, 'Little did we know, either!'

At the end of the afternoon, we stood on the vicarage steps to wave Moth and Helen off in their taxi at the beginning of a fortnight in the Dordogne and a lifetime in married bliss.

Charles lifted Sophie up on his arm. 'Bye-bye, Mummy!' she cried. 'Bye-bye, Daddy-Moth!'

I think that's when I came closest to bursting into tears, only I felt a tug on my coat.

'Mum. Can I change into my jeans now? These trousers are ever so tight.'

'Of course you can change, Josh. And I'll alter those grey ones of Drew's for you before school starts.'

Charles put his free arm round my shoulder and kissed my cheek. 'Fancy a cup of tea? Sophie and I will put the kettle on. You go and put your feet up.'

Also by Brenda Courtie

❊ her own story ❊

Not Quite Heaven

Sometimes God takes a life and, over the years, moulds it so gently to his purpose that it is only on looking back that a pattern can be discerned.

Brenda Courtie travelled a long way to cover the two miles from the Bootle docks where she was born to Hatton Hill, the 'heaven' of her childhood fancy. Along the way, she found a personal faith in Christ, and learned to use for God the gifts he has given her — of music, from classical to jazz; of marriage and motherhood, and friendship; as well as the gift of the Spirit by which God made himself known to her in a special way.

Back in her native Merseyside — not quite heaven, perhaps — she found a new use for her gifts as a vicar's wife, and a new ministry, telling the Good News as a talented writer and broadcaster.

More books from

TRI∧NGLE

CORRIE TEN BOOM
Clippings from my Notebook
Her own selection from her devotional writings

Not I, but Christ
A collection of her devotional broadcast talks

FRANK COLQUHOUN
Family Prayers
Prayers for use at home and for all situations

PATRICIA CORNWELL
A Time for Remembering — The Ruth Graham story
An intimate biography of this remarkable Christian woman,
wife of evangelist Billy Graham.

MARGARET CUNDIFF
Called to be Me
Often hilarious, sometimes poignant, always entertaining —
her reminiscences of ten years as a deaconess in a North
Yorkshire parish.

Living by the Book
A personal journey through the Sermon on the Mount

ERIC LIDDELL
The Disciplines of the Christian Life
First publication of this newly-discovered work by the hero of
Chariots of Fire. A practical guide to Christian living

DIANA PECK
There's Somebody at the Door
The entertaining and challenging story of a family who kept
'open house' in the service of Christ.